THE CHEMISTRY OF THE LANTHANIDES

Selected Topics in Modern Chemistry

SERIES EDITORS

Professor Harry H. Sisler
Department of Chemistry
University of Florida

Professor Calvin A. VanderWerf
Department of Chemistry
University of Kansas

Published

EYRING AND EYRING—*Modern Chemical Kinetics*
KIEFFER—*The Mole Concept in Chemistry*
MOELLER—*The Chemistry of the Lanthanides*
OVERMAN—*Basic Concepts of Nuclear Chemistry*
RYSCHKEWITSCH—*Chemical Bonding and the Geometry of Molecules*
SISLER—*Chemistry in Non-Aqueous Solvents*
VANDERWERF—*Acids, Bases, and the Chemistry of the Covalent Bond*

In Press

HILDEBRAND—*An Introduction to Molecular Kinetic Theory*
SISLER—*Structure, Properties, and the Periodic Law*

(Many additional titles are in preparation.)

Series Editors' Statement

When a master teacher of chemistry, known for his lucid writing, has free rein to present the area in which he is a world-renowned research expert, the result is certain to be engrossing. And when that area is one which uniquely illustrates the application of certain principles of chemistry, the product is bound to be of utmost value and usefulness.

Professor Moeller's appealing and representative vignette of modern inorganic chemistry is all this and more. The fun Dr. Moeller had in writing "The Chemistry of the Lanthanides" will be mirrored by your enjoyment as you read it. And in the reading you will acquire a clearer insight into many basic relationships between atomic structure and properties of the elements.

You will discover also that a thorough understanding of the lanthanides provides the ideal approach to the fascinating chemistry of the actinides. And, just as important, you will find completely infectious the author's spirit of research—his enthusiasm for the challenge and lure of the unsolved· problem and the unanswered question.

As editors we are proud to add Professor Moeller's book, a thoroughly readable blending of fact and principle, to SELECTED TOPICS IN MODERN CHEMISTRY. We are confident that you will find it interesting, stimulating, and useful.

Harry H. Sisler
Calvin A. VanderWerf

THE CHEMISTRY OF
THE LANTHANIDES

THERALD MOELLER

Professor of Inorganic Chemistry
University of Illinois
Urbana, Illinois

New York
REINHOLD PUBLISHING CORPORATION
Chapman & Hall, Ltd., London

Library of Congress Catalog Card Number: 63-9651
Printed in the United States of America

PREFACE

There is sufficient of the unexpected, the unpredicted, and the unusual in most chemistry to make its study and practice a fascinating experience. Each of these terms aptly describes the type of chemistry that provides the basis for this small volume. In a sense, each also describes the preparation of "The Chemistry of the Lanthanides," for little did the author realize that a seminar assignment in this area received in graduate school would both open to him an interesting region for subsequent research and provide him ultimately with the incentive to prepare this manuscript. If a perusal of this account provides the reader with both information and an appreciation of the intriguing problems that remain to be solved, the author will count the intervening years as usefully spent.

"The Chemistry of the Lanthanides" is more than a mere description of the behavior of a series of elements. It is also a presentation of the theoretical principles that can be invoked to account for this behavior and a discussion of the applications and limitations of these principles. In this sense, it is a representative fragment of modern inorganic chemistry, for inorganic chemistry in its truest sense is a balanced and reasonable combination of fact and principle where the former is used to test and support or negate the latter. The lanthanides, because of their marked similarities and generally uniform changes in properties with change in atomic number, are ideal subjects for such a presentation and serve well to introduce the beginning student to a variety of useful principles.

The past several years have witnessed a somewhat dramatic rebirth of interest in the lanthanides. In part, this has stemmed from the general renaissance that has characterized inorganic chemistry as a whole; in part, it has come from the search for new materials with new properties that are essential to solving the many problems of our expanding technology; in part, also, it has arisen from the realization that the chemistry of plutonium and the other transuranium species could best be approached by way of a thorough understanding of that of the only other truly analogous elements, the lanthanides. Our presentation, then, is a blend of traditional observation with the modern, followed by a projection to the heavy elements. If the order followed appears, on occasion, somewhat unconventional, it is the result of the author's conviction that the importance of this blend requires a logical, but not necessarily chronological, development of ideas.

To name all of those whose research contributions and whose friendly and stimulating discussions have provided the author with the background for this discussion would be impossibly difficult. The author can do no more than say "Thank you" to each, with the hope that in such a simple way he can indicate the depth of his gratitude. He is, of course, indebted particularly to the late Professor B. Smith Hopkins of the University of Illinois—that fine gentleman, able investigator, and outstanding teacher who first provided him with purified materials for research and encouraged him at the incidence of his academic career.

The author is deeply grateful to Miss Jeanne C. Hammer for her very substantial assistance in preparing the manuscript.

THERALD MOELLER

Urbana, Illinois
February, 1963

CONTENTS

CONTENTS

chapter one

INTRODUCTION—AN ERA OF DISCOVERY, CONFUSION, AND ELUCIDATION

What has developed into a fascinating realm of chemistry embracing both a series of naturally occurring elements of extraordinary similarity and a closely comparable series of synthetically produced elements of rather remarkable properties had its origin in the somewhat accidental discovery by Swedish Army Lieutenant C. A. Arrhenius in 1787 of an unusual black mineral specimen at a quarry at Ytterby, a small community not far from Stockholm. When, in 1794, Johan Gadolin, a Finnish chemist at the University of Åbo, separated from samples of this mineral about 38% of a new and previously undescribed "earth" (or *oxide*, in our more modern terminology), the basis for a series of investigations extending through the present was unwittingly laid. It remained only for A. G. Ekeberg, at Uppsala, to suggest in 1797 the name *gadolinite* for the mineral and the name *yttria* for the new earth.

Shortly thereafter (in 1803), M. H. Klaproth, a German investigator, and, independently, J. J. Berzelius, the renowned

Swedish chemist, and his collaborator Wilhelm Hisinger isolated from a heavy mineral (originally found in 1871 in a mine at Bastnäs, Sweden, by A. F. Cronstedt) another similar and yet somewhat different earth. This was named *ceria*, after the then recently discovered planetoid Ceres, and the mineral *cerite*.

It was believed at the time that both yttria and ceria were derived from single elements. Yet subsequent study showed each to be a complex mixture of oxides, the complete simplification of which required more than a century of effort. This was an era of substantially blind experimentation complicated by a lack of understanding of why these substances are so closely similar, no appreciation of even how many elemental species might be involved, and a lack of positive experimental means of absolute identification of supposedly pure samples. If errors were made—and there were many—and if confusion arose—as it did in many instances—we may and should nevertheless pay tribute to the perserverance of the host of investigators who succeeded ultimately in unraveling one of the most complicated of all chemical problems.

The Simplification of Ceria and Yttria

Proof of the ultimate complexity of both ceria and yttria was given many years after their isolation by C. G. Mosander, a Swedish surgeon, chemist, and mineralogist, who was for a time an assistant to Berzelius. During the period 1839–1841, Mosander thermally decomposed a nitrate obtained from ceria and treated the product with dilute nitric acid. From the resulting solution, he then isolated first a new earth, *lanthana*, and then later another new earth, *didymia* (the twin brother of lanthana), of similar chemical, but slightly different physical properties. Similarly, in 1843, Mosander separated from the original yttria three oxide fractions: one white (*yttria*), one yellow (old *erbia*), and one rose-colored (old *terbia*).

There was again an extensive period of intense but unproductive activity, which then culminated in the partial and finally ultimate simplification of these two complex oxides. The more significant developments, including the names of the principal investigators and the origin of the names of the numerous elements, are summarized in Tables 1.1 and 1.2. The striking parallels between the investigations of the two oxides are at once apparent, as are, of course, certain items of confusion. One of the most significant of the latter concerns the reversal of names of erbia and terbia (Table 1.2), which prompts the distinction old erbia vs. new erbia and old terbia vs. new terbia. In both of these tables, the earth names are used for mixtures and the modern names of the elements, together with their symbols, for separated and clearly identified species.

Tables 1.1 and 1.2 cannot begin to suggest the complexities of the problems encountered. There was an understandable confusion among other names, prompted of course by the poor communication among workers in the 19th and early 20th centuries. The reported discovery of elements other than those now accepted was not uncommon. Although these often proved to be mixtures, on occasion more than one worker independently isolated the same material. Cases in point include gadolinium (first isolated from yttria by the Swiss chemist de Marignac in 1880 and later, in 1885, obtained from ceria by the French investigator de Boisbaudran) and lutetium (announced in 1907 by the Frenchman Urbain but obtained nearly simultaneously by both the Austrian von Welsbach and the American James). Tables 1.1 and 1.2 do serious injustice to the countless other workers who contributed data that aided materially in making possible the discoveries outlined.

TABLE 1.1. The Simplification of Ceria*

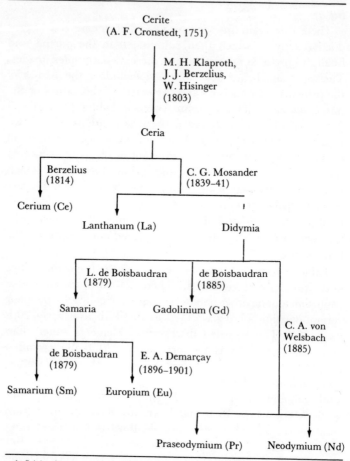

* *Origin of names:*   lanthanum—to lie hidden; cerium—planetoid Ceres; praseodymium—green twin; neodymium—new twin; samarium—mineral samarskite;
europium—Europe; gadolinium—Gadolin.

TABLE 1.2. The Simplification of Yttria*

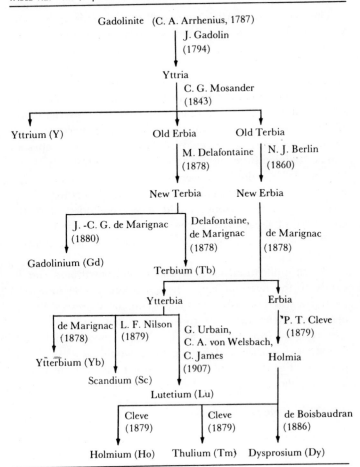

* *Origin of names:* yttrium, ytterbium, erbium, terbium—Ytterby; gadolinium—Gadolin; dysprosium—difficult of access; holmium—Stockholm; thulium—Thule (ancient name of Scandinavia); lutetium—Lutetia (ancient name of Paris); scandium—Scandinavia.

Some Consequences and Conclusions

The striking similarities among the compounds of the fourteen new elements so characterized required that the crystallization, precipitation, thermal decomposition, and extraction procedures used for their separation all be fractional in character. Although two markedly different substances can ordinarily be separated in a single step, closely similar substances cannot. Rather, a single step does no more than alter slightly the ratio between the two, and a given operation must be repeated many times before slight differences in properties can be sufficiently magnified to effect a separation. With the lanthanides, hundreds (or even thousands) of steps were often required for ultimate separation. It is not surprising, therefore, that many persons should have concluded that the chemistry of separations is the only important chemistry of these elements, nor, perhaps, that such a misconception should still persist.

The simplification of yttria and ceria contributed significantly to the development of new laboratory and industrial techniques and of instrumental methods of analysis. Prominent among the latter are those of emission and absorption spectroscopy (pp. 15, 25, 29–33, 74), without which confirmation of purity and homogeneity would have been impossible. The factual information gained has been invaluable in testing modern theoretical interpretations.

A Problem of Nomenclature and Scarcity

Because the elements of this series were obtained originally as earths (oxides) from relatively rare minerals, they were characterized as *rare earths*. Although this name is still used, it is an unfortunate one because of its implications. Crustal abundance data, as summarized in Table 1.3, indicate clearly that the lanthanides are at least as abundant as many of the commoner elements and that over-all supplies are potentially unlimited. That this is seldom appreciated is convincing proof that a scientific idea, once advanced, is never easy to dispel, regardless of its lack of merit.

TABLE 1.3. Abundances of Elements in Igneous Rocks of Crust of the Earth

Symbol	Atomic number	Abundance, g./metric ton	Symbol	Atomic number	Abundance, g./metric ton
Sc	21	5	Be	4	6
Y	39	28.1	B	5	<3
La	57	18.3	N	7	46.3
Ce	58	46.1	Co	27	23
Pr	59	5.53	Cu	29	70
Nd	60	23.9	Ga	31	15
Pm	61	ca. 0	Ge	32	7
Sm	62	6.47	As	33	5
Eu	63	1.06	Br	35	1.62
Gd	64	6.36	Mo	42	2.5–15
Tb	65	0.91	Ag	47	0.1
Dy	66	4.47	Cd	48	0.15
Ho	67	1.15	Sn	50	40
Er	68	2.47	Sb	51	1
Tm	69	0.2	I	53	0.1
Yb	70	2.66	Pb	82	16
Lu	71	0.75	Bi	83	0.2

At the present, the name *lanthanides* is preferred for these elements. This derives, of course, from lanthanum, the first of the elements of the series in order of increasing atomic number. For reasons that are discussed later (pp. 20–25), we include yttrium as a lanthanide, although it differs significantly in atomic weight (p. 37) and other properties (pp. 58–59). Other names in use are *lanthanide elements*, *lanthanons*, and *f-type transition elements*. The significance of the last of these is brought out in Chapter 2.

Element 61—Will-o'-the-Wisp or Actuality?

A comparison of the elements listed in Tables 1.1 and 1.2 with those in Table 1.3, where atomic numbers are given, shows that thus far we have given no information on element 61, i.e., the element that should appear between neodymium and samarium.

None of the investigations previously outlined gave any indication of the existence of such an element in the materials recovered. It is significant, however, that in 1902 Bohuslav Brauner, of the Bohemian University in Prague, suggested that such an element should exist. With the development of information on electronic configurations (pp. 13–16), the reasonableness of this prediction became evident, and several exhaustive searches were made, using largely neodymium-samarium fractions where this element might most logically be expected to concentrate. Although these were notably unsuccessful, in 1926, B. S. Hopkins, L. F. Yntema, and J. A. Harris, of the University of Illinois, and L. Rolla and L. Fernandes, of the Royal University in Florence, Italy, independently offered spectroscopic evidence for the existence of the element in minute quantities in various concentrates. The names *illinium* and *florentium* were proposed by these two groups, respectively. Subsequent research has failed to confirm these findings. In 1947, J. A. Marinsky, L. E. Glendenin, and C. D. Coryell reported the ion-exchange separation and identification (p. 81) of an isotope of this element, using materials obtained at Oak Ridge, Tennessee, from the fission of uranium. Subsequently, many grams of its salts have been recovered from this source. The name *promethium* (from Prometheus) is now universally accepted.

Inasmuch as small quantities of uranium are always undergoing fission, one cannot deny the absolute existence of promethium in nature. The isotopes so obtained—and, in

TABLE 1.4. Isotopes of Promethium

Mass number	Type of decay[*]	Half-life	Source
141	β^+	20 min.	
142	β^+	30 sec.	Daughter ^{142}Sm
143	EC, γ	270 days	
144	EC, γ	300 days	
145	β^+	16 days	
	EC, γ	18 yr.	Daughter ^{145}Sm
146	β^-	ca. 1 yr.	
147	β^-, γ	2.64 yr.	Fission ^{235}U
148	β^-, γ	42 days	
149	β^-, γ	54 hr.	Daughter ^{149}Nd
150	β^-, γ	2.7 hr.	
151	β^-, γ	27.5 hr.	Daughter ^{151}Nd

[*] EC = electron capture.

fact, all known isotopes of the element—decay spontaneously (Table 1.4) with such short half-lives[*] that it seems highly improbable that sufficient promethium could exist in nature to permit its chemical isolation. However, until it has been shown clearly that no stable or very long-lived isotope can exist, that no natural decay process (beyond fission) is continually generating a promethium isotope, and that exact repetition under carefully controlled conditions of the experiments upon which claims of isolation were based gives negative results, we cannot conclude with absolute scientific accuracy that recovery of compounds of this element from a natural source is impossible.

In any event, fission-product promethium is a true lanthanide, with properties intermediate between those of neodymium and samarium.

[*] Each radioactive, or spontaneously unstable, isotope has a characteristic half-life, or time necessary for one-half of the quantity present to disintegrate. Unless a species is continuously generated, it cannot occur in nature if its half-life is less than the age of the earth, i.e., about 10^9 years.

Close Relatives—The Actinides

Of all the other elements, only those with atomic numbers 89–103 (i.e., actinium through lawrencium, or the actinides) resemble the lanthanides closely in all characteristics. Only the lightest of these elements exist in nature. The others must be obtained synthetically, and such processes may yield only a few atoms of product. Fortunately, it has been possible to use the known chemistry of the lanthanides to develop the chemistry of the actinides.

Recapitulation—and Then?

We have chosen to introduce the chemistry of the lanthanides in such a fashion as to raise many questions in your mind. Among these must be at least the following:

1. Why do we have such a series of closely related elements?
2. Can we account logically for both the distinct similarities and slight differences noted among these elements and their compounds?
3. How can we classify these elements in the Periodic Table?
4. To what extent can we account for differences between these elements and other elements?
5. Why do we have another series of elements (the actinides) that resembles the lanthanides?
6. What advances have been made subsequent to those outlined above?
7. To what extent can we take practical advantage of the apparently different properties that must characterize this series?

It will be our purpose in subsequent chapters to provide answers to these and other questions. To a fair degree, this may be done by developing first some principles based largely upon atomic structures. This we do in Chapter 2.

Selected Readings

Boyd, G. E., *J. Chem. Educ.*, **36,** 3–14 (1959). (Promethium.)

Spencer, J. F., "The Metals of the Rare Earths," ch. I, Longmans, Green, London, 1919. (History.)

Vickery, R. C., "Chemistry of the Lanthanons," ch. 1, Academic Press, New York, 1953. (History.)

Weeks, M. E., "Discovery of the Elements," 6th ed., chs. 26, 31, The Journal of Chemical Education, Easton, Pa., 1956. (History.)

Yost, D. M., Russell, H., Jr., and Garner, C. S., "The Rare-Earth Elements and Their Compounds," ch. 4, John Wiley & Sons, New York, 1947. (Promethium.)

chapter two

ATOMIC STRUCTURE AND ITS CONSEQUENCES—THE DAWN OF UNDERSTANDING

If, as is suggested by the developments outlined in Chapter 1, there is an essential uniqueness in the chemistry of the lanthanides, it must, as we now know, reside in the structures of their individual atoms and ions. From modern extensions of Niels Bohr's 1913 theory of the hydrogen atom we know that as the complexity of the nucleus is increased as a result of addition of protons (and neutrons), each of the electrons needed to preserve electroneutrality seeks out not only the least energetic of the possible principal quantum levels available but also the least energetic of the several possible subsidiary levels, or *orbitals*, within that principal level. It is thus feasible to classify the elements in terms of the electronic configurations characterizing these low-energy, or *ground-state*, arrangements, and to distinguish groups of elements of potentially (and actually) similar properties in terms of observed similarities in ground-state configuration.

Electronic Configurations of the Lanthanides

The over-all properties of the lanthanides suggest that they are members of a subgroup within Periodic Group III (i.e., family IIIb). The ground-state electronic configurations

Sc $\ \mathcal{Z} = 21\ \ 1s^2 2s^2 2p^6 3s^2 3p^6 3d^1 4s^2$
     or Ar core $+\ 3d^1 4s^2$

Y $\ \mathcal{Z} = 39\ \ 1s^2 2s^2 2p^6 3s^2 3p^6 3d^{10} 4s^2 4p^6 4d^1 5s^2$
     or Kr core $+\ 4d^1 5s^2$

La $\ \mathcal{Z} = 57\ \ 1s^2 2s^2 2p^6 3s^2 3p^6 3d^{10} 4s^2 4p^6 4d^{10} 5s^2 5p^6 5d^1 6s^2$
     or Xe core $+\ 5d^1 6s^2$

Ac $\ \mathcal{Z} = 89\ \ 1s^2 2s^2 2p^6 3s^2 3p^6 3d^{10} 4s^2 4p^6 4d^{10} 4f^{14} 5s^2 5p^6 5d^{10} 6s^2 6p^6 6d^1 7s^2$
     or Rn core $+\ 6d^1 7s^2$

indicate clearly that the elements usually listed in this family are the first members of the four d-type transition series. After scandium and yttrium, the electrons required to give elements of steadily increasing atomic number are added, respectively, to the $3d$ and $4d$ levels, and the remaining elements of the first and second transition series thus result. After lanthanum, however, the energy of the $4f$ level falls below that of the $5d$, and subsequent electrons are thus added to the inner, shielded $4f$ orbitals. Inasmuch as there are seven such orbitals, each with a capacity of two electrons,[*] a total of 14 elements of this *inner* or f-type transition series may then result before the $5d$ orbitals can again fill regularly. This accounts for the elements cerium through lutetium ($\mathcal{Z} = 58$–71) and requires that hafnium ($\mathcal{Z} = 72$, $4f^{14} 5d^2 6s^2$) be a strict electronic analog of zirconium ($\mathcal{Z} = 40$, $4d^2 5s^2$) and not a lanthanide. A similar situation exists after actinium (p. 99), with

---

[*] That each orbital can have two electrons is a consequence of the fact that two electrons may be alike in all properties except spin about the r own axes. The Hund Principle of Maximum Multiplicity requires that within a given set of orbitals (here $4f$) each orbital must be occupied singly before any pairing of electrons through double occupancy can occur.

preferential occupancy of the $5f$ orbitals thus accounting for the actinides.

Although it is implied that the $4f$ orbitals are occupied regularly, the data in Table 2.1 show clearly that this is not exactly true. Instead, there is a distinct tendency for the f orbitals to be occupied in preference to maintaining the

TABLE 2.1   Ground-State Electronic Configurations of Atoms

Element	Atomic number (Z)	Configuration	
		Idealized	Observed[*]
Sc	21	$3d^1 4s^2$	$3d^1 4s^2$
Y	39	$4d^1 5s^2$	$4d^1 5s^2$
La	57	$5d^1 6s^2$	$5d^1 6s^2$
Ce	58	$4f^1 \ 5d^1 6s^2$	$4f^1 \ 5d^1 6s^2$
Pr	59	$4f^2 \ 5d^1 6s^2$	$4f^3 \qquad 6s^2$
Nd	60	$4f^3 \ 5d^1 6s^2$	$4f^4 \qquad 6s^2$
Pm	61	$4f^4 \ 5d^1 6s^2$	$4f^5 \qquad 6s^2$
Sm	62	$4f^5 \ 5d^1 6s^2$	$4f^6 \qquad 6s^2$
Eu	63	$4f^6 \ 5d^1 6s^2$	$4f^7 \qquad 6s^2$
Gd	64	$4f^7 \ 5d^1 6s^2$	$4f^7 \ 5d^1 6s^2$
Tb	65	$4f^8 \ 5d^1 6s^2$	$4f^9 \qquad 6s^2$
			(or $4f^8 5d^1 6s^2$)
Dy	66	$4f^9 \ 5d^1 6s^2$	$4f^{10} \qquad 6s^2$
Ho	67	$4f^{10} 5d^1 6s^2$	$4f^{11} \qquad 6s^2$
Er	68	$4f^{11} 5d^1 6s^2$	$4f^{12} \qquad 6s^2$
Tm	69	$4f^{12} 5d^1 6s^2$	$4f^{13} \qquad 6s^2$
Yb	70	$4f^{13} 5d^1 6s^2$	$4f^{14} \qquad 6s^2$
Lu	71	$4f^{14} 5d^1 6s^2$	$4f^{14} 5d^1 6s^2$

[*] Cunningham, B. B., "Rare Earth Research," E. V. Kleber, Ed., pp. 127–30, The Macmillan Company, New York, 1961.

$4f^n 5d^1$ arrangement that such an idealized picture would require. This tendency is a reflection of the enhanced electronic stability that is associated with complete single (here $4f^7$) or complete double (here $4f^{14}$) occupancy of any set of orbitals. Thus, the $4f^7$ and $4f^{14}$ arrangements are achieved as soon as possible (at europium and ytterbium, respectively). Gadolinium, at the exact center of the series, has the expected $4f^7 5d^1 6s^2$ ground-state configuration.

Electronic configurations are most commonly established experimentally as interpretations of observed emission spectra. This technique is based on the fact that each line in an emission spectrum reflects the energy change involved in the transition of an electron from one energy level to another. If the spectrum contains only a few lines, its interpretation is comparatively easy, and an unambiguous ground-state configuration can be established for the atom in question. If, as is true with many of the lanthanides, the spectrum is highly complex, the establishment of an absolutely correct configuration is extremely difficult. The problem with the lanthanides concerns primarily the presence or absence of a $5d$ electron. This arises, of course, from the fact that the $5d$ and $4f$ orbitals have so nearly the same energy that distinction between the two is difficult. The configurations summarized in Table 2.1 are the best available from spectroscopic and atomic beam resonance data. It is probable that no more than minor changes in them will be made as a result of future studies.

Whether the fundamental configuration is $4f^n 5d^1 6s^2$ or $4f^{n+1} 6s^2$ is of far less chemical than physical significance, since the energy differences are too small to alter many chemical properties. To some extent, lanthanum and lutetium are cases in point, since their observed chemical characteristics are nearly the same as those of the adjacent lanthanides.

That such similar electronic configurations should result in striking similarities among the chemical properties of the lanthanides is both reasonable and in keeping with experimental observation. The $4f$ electrons differentiating the several elements from one another are sufficiently well shielded by intervening electron shells as to be largely unavailable for chemical interaction, and this feature distinguishes the lanthanides from the d-type transition elements, in which the d electrons are the "outermost" or valence electrons and are involved when chemical reactions occur.

The fundamental similarity in "outer" electronic configuration between the lanthanides and scandium, yttrium, and actinium favors classification of all these elements together in the same periodic family. The physical limitations of the Periodic Table as it is usually drawn, however, result in our placing the lanthanides (and actinides) apart from the remaining elements. Neither scandium nor yttrium is properly a lanthanide, as far as electronic configuration is concerned, nor properly is lanthanum since it has no 4*f* electrons. Property-wise, as has been indicated and will be shown further in the next section, yttrium and lanthanum are better discussed with the lanthanides than with any other elements. Scandium, on the other hand, is markedly different (p. 24). Even though scandium was first isolated from yttria sources (Table 1.2), its primary mode of natural occurrence is not with the lanthanides.

Some Indirect Consequences of Electronic Configuration

Certain of the questions (1, 3, 5) raised in Chapter 1 have now been answered solely in terms of the ground-state electronic configurations of the atoms. The answers to others may be obtained on a similar basis, but somewhat less directly. Two of these relate to the marked similarities among compounds that puzzled early workers and the slight differences that enabled these workers to effect separations.

Oxidation States. It was observed even during pioneering studies that in their commonest compounds the lanthanides are uniformly *tripositive*. It is true that early investigators recognized *tetrapositive* cerium and higher-valent praseodymium and terbium as the dark-colored oxides Pr_6O_{11} and Tb_4O_7, but it was not until the 20th century that *dipositive* europium, ytterbium, and samarium were characterized.

Indeed, it was not until the 1950's that truly praseodymium(IV) and terbium(IV) compounds were described and not until the 1960's that tetrapositive neodymium and dysprosium and dipositive cerium, neodymium, and thulium were obtained. Of the nontripositive states, only tetrapositive cerium, praseodymium, and terbium and dipositive samarium, europium, and ytterbium have sufficient chemical stability to be of importance. Yttrium is always tripositive in its compounds.

That direct correlation between oxidation state and electronic configuration is the exception rather than the rule is shown by the data in Table 2.2. Inasmuch as the $6s^2$ configuration is the most generally characteristic one for the lanthanides (Table 2.1), a uniform dipositive state might be expected. Furthermore, although the removal of an additional $5d$ electron, by analogy to what occurs with d-type transition elements, might be reasonable, the cases where this is possible are obviously limited. Penetration of the $4f$ arrangement is

TABLE 2.2. Distinguishing Electronic Configurations for Observed Oxidation States

Symbol	Configuration		
	+2	+3	+4
La		$4f^0$ (La^{3+})	
Ce	$4f^2$ ($CeCl_2$)	$4f^1$ (Ce^{3+})	$4f^0$ (Ce^{4+})
Pr		$4f^2$ (Pr^{3+})	$4f^1$ (PrO_2, Na_2PrF_6)
Nd	$4f^4$ (NdI_2)	$4f^3$ (Nd^{3+})	$4f^2$ (Cs_3NdF_7)
Pm		$4f^4$ (Pm^{3+})	
Sm	$4f^6$ (Sm^{2+})	$4f^5$ (Sm^{3+})	
Eu	$4f^7$ (Eu^{2+})	$4f^6$ (Eu^{3+})	
Gd		$4f^7$ (Gd^{3+})	
Tb		$4f^8$ (Tb^{3+})	$4f^7$ (TbO_2, TbF_4)
Dy		$4f^9$ (Dy^{3+})	$4f^8$ (Cs_3DyF_7)
Ho		$4f^{10}$ (Ho^{3+})	
Er		$4f^{11}$ (Er^{3+})	
Tm	$4f^{13}$ (TmI_2)	$4f^{12}$ (Tm^{3+})	
Yb	$4f^{14}$ (Yb^{2+})	$4f^{13}$ (Yb^{3+})	
Lu		$4f^{14}$ (Lu^{3+})	

thus essential, but why should this result preferentially in the tripositive state for all the elements?

This question can be answered only qualitatively. If the tripositive state is the preferred one in aqueous solution, then oxidation, as represented by the equation (Ln = any lanthanide)

$$Ln^{3+}(aq) + \tfrac{1}{4}O_2(g) + H^+(aq) \rightleftharpoons Ln^{4+}(aq) + \tfrac{1}{2}H_2O(l)$$

or reduction, as represented by the equation

$$Ln^{3+}(aq) + \tfrac{1}{2}H_2(g) \rightleftharpoons Ln^{2+}(aq) + H^+(aq)$$

must be unfavorable. It can be shown, although the treatment is more involved than we need consider here, that the conversion from one oxidation state to another in aqueous solution is controlled by the magnitudes of the energy required to remove an electron from the gaseous ion in its lower oxidation state (i.e., *ionization energy*) and of the energies released when the two gaseous ions combine with water to form the aquated species (*energy of hydration*). Calculation on this basis shows that in solution, all tetrapositive species (except possibly Ce^{4+}) and all dipositive species (except Eu^{2+}) must revert to the tripositive. This leads to the conclusion that the tripositive state owes its general stability to a somewhat fortuitous combination of ionization and hydration energies rather than to any particular electronic configuration.

Similarly, oxidation and reduction among solid compounds can be related to the magnitudes of the ionization energy and the energy released when the gaseous ions combine to produce crystalline solids (i.e., the *lattice* or *crystal energy*). Again, a fortuitous combination of these renders the tripositive state the most common, but the energy conditions are more favorable to the existence of nontripositive species (Table 2.2) in the solid state than in solution.

The ease of formation of the various oxidation states in solu-

TABLE 2.3.   Standard Oxidation Potential Data[*] for Acidic Solutions

Symbol	E°_{298}, v.	Symbol	E°_{298}, v.
	Couples $Ln^0 - Ln^{III}$		
	$Ln(s) \rightleftharpoons Ln^{3+}(aq) + 3e^-$		
Y	+2.37	Gd	+2.40
La	2.52	Tb	2.39
Ce	2.48	Dy	2.35
Pr	2.47	Ho	2.32
Nd	2.44	Er	2.30
Pm	2.42	Tm	2.28
Sm	2.41	Yb	2.27
Eu	2.41	Lu	2.25
	Couples $Ln^{II} - Ln^{III}$		
	$Ln^{2+}(aq) \rightleftharpoons Ln^{3+}(aq) + e^-$		
Sm	+1.55	Yb	+1.15
Eu	0.43		
	Couples $Ln^{III} - Ln^{IV}$		
	$Ln^{3+}(aq) \rightleftharpoons Ln^{4+}(aq) + e^-$		
Ce	−1.74	Pr	−2.86

[*] Estimated, in many cases.

tion is indicated by the standard oxidation potential data summarized in Table 2.3. It is apparent that the elemental lanthanides are very powerful reducing agents and that oxidation to the tripositive state occurs readily and vigorously. The enhanced stabilities of the empty, half-filled, and completely filled $4f$ arrangements are also indicated by these data. Thus cerium(IV), with its $4f^0$ configuration, is much less readily reduced to the tripositive state than the $4f^1$ species praseodymium(IV). Furthermore, the $4f^7$ species europium(II) and the $4f^{14}$ species ytterbium(II) are the weakest reducing agents of the dipositive species. The preponderance of $4f^0$ species (La^{III}, Ce^{IV}), $4f^7$ species (Eu^{II}, Gd^{III}, Tb^{IV}), and $4f^{14}$ species (Yb^{II}, Lu^{III}) supports this general relationship.

Size Relationships.   The sizes of atoms and ions are determined both by nuclear charge and by the number and degree
of occupancy of electronic shells.   Both of these factors are
reflected in the data for atomic and crystal (ionic) radii summarized in Table 2.4.   Thus, among either the metals Sc, Y,
La or the ions Sc^{3+}, Y^{3+}, La^{3+} there is a steady increase in size
with increase in atomic number, corresponding to the fact that
addition of electrons to higher and higher energy levels over-
comes increasing contractive effects that result from the enhanced attraction produced by larger nuclear charge.   In the
series La–Lu or La^{3+}–Lu^{3+}, however, a general decrease in
size with increase in atomic number results because addition
of electrons to the shielded $4f$ orbitals cannot compensate for
the effect of increased nuclear charge.   A similar but more
limited trend characterizes the nontripositive ions.   These

TABLE 2.4.   Size Relationships

Symbol	Atomic number	Atomic radius,[*] Å.	Crystal or ionic radius, Å.		
			Ln^{2+}	Ln^{3+}	Ln^{4+}
Sc	21	1.641		0.68	
Y	39	1.801		0.88	
La	57	1.877		1.061	
Ce	58	1.82		1.034	0.92
Pr	59	1.828		1.013	0.90
Nd	60	1.821		0.995	
Pm	61	—		(0.979)	
Sm	62	1.802	1.11	0.964	
Eu	63	2.042	1.09	0.950	
Gd	64	1.802		0.938	
Tb	65	1.782		0.923	0.84
Dy	66	1.773		0.908	
Ho	67	1.766		0.894	
Er	68	1.757		0.881	
Tm	69	1.746	0.94	0.869	
Yb	70	1.940	0.93	0.858	
Lu	71	1.734		0.848	

[*] For structures in which each atom has 12 other atoms as nearest neighbors.

decreases are known as the *Lanthanide Contraction*. The general decrease in crystal radius from Ln^{2+} to Ln^{3+} to Ln^{4+} reflects increasing cationic charge.

As indicated in Fig. 2.1, the lanthanide contraction is essen-

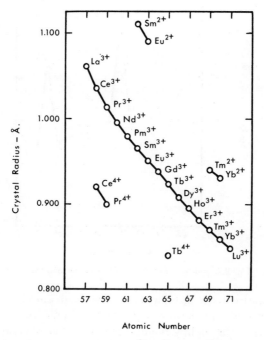

Fig. 2.1. Crystal radii of Ln^{2+}, Ln^{3+}, and Ln^{4+} ions.

tially parallel among the di-, tri-, and tetrapositive ions. A slight, but detectable, discontinuity among the tripositive ions appears at gadolinium. Fig. 2.2 shows the contraction among the metals, but indicates dramatically the large atomic radii of europium and ytterbium. It is believed that these seemingly anomalous values reflect a tendency for these two elements to

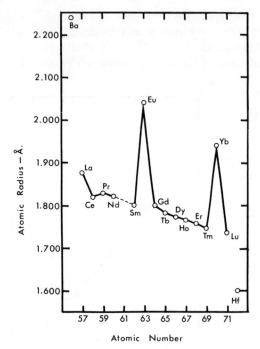

Fig. 2.2. Atomic radii of lanthanides, barium, and hafnium.

be dipositive in the metallic state. The rough parallel between these metals and barium supports this contention. Correspondingly, the slightly reduced atomic radius of cerium may suggest a tetravalent state (compare hafnium, Fig. 2.2).

Atomic and ionic radii affect those properties of the metals and their cations, respectively, that reflect attraction or lack of attraction for electrons and anions, i.e., properties of *basicity*. Broadly, basicity is a measure of the ease with which a species loses electrons or of the lack of attraction which a cation has for electrons or anions. Thus, radii are important in terms of both (1) their absolute magnitudes and (2) their change with atomic number.

1. *Consequences of Numerical Magnitude.* Both the atoms and their derived cations are comparatively large (Table 2.5). Observations that the elemental lanthanides are powerful reducing agents (Table 2.3), comparable in strength to the alkaline earth metals and greater in strength than most metals that yield tripositive ions, correlate well with the large atomic radii. Observations that compounds of the lanthanides have

TABLE 2.5. Some Comparative Atomic and Crystal Radii (Ångstrom units)

Type of radius	Lanthanides		Nonlanthanides	
Atomic	La	1.877	Al	1.248
	Gd	1.802	Fe	1.165
	Lu	1.734	Ca	1.736
	Eu	2.042	Sr	1.914
	Yb	1.940	Ba	1.981
Crystal (M^{2+})	Sm	1.11	Fe	0.74
	Eu	1.09	Ca	0.99
	Tm	0.94	Sr	1.12
	Yb	0.92	Ba	1.34
Crystal (M^{3+})	La	1.061	Al	0.51
	Gd	0.938	Cr	0.63
	Lu	0.848	Fe	0.64
			Ac	1.11
Crystal (M^{4+})	Ce	0.92	Zr	0.79
	Pr	0.90	Hf	0.78
	Tb	0.84	Th	0.99
			U	0.93

pronounced ionic character and that complex species are limited correlate with the reduced attractions for anions and polar groups resulting from large cationic radii. The close parallel suggested between the dipositive species and the heavier alkaline earth metal ions is supported by experimental observation (pp. 44–45). The large tripositive ions resemble strikingly only the comparably sized actinide ions (pp. 101, 104).

Similarly, cerium(IV) resembles tetrapositive thorium and uranium but not zirconium and hafnium.

2. *Consequences of the Lanthanide Contraction.* These include the position of yttrium, variations in properties among the lanthanides, and variations in properties among the species that follow the lanthanides in atomic number.

The magnitude of the lanthanide contraction is such that the crystal radius of the Y^{3+} ion is reached in the holmium-erbium region. The resulting similarity in size, coupled of course with equality in ionic charge, accounts reasonably for the invariable natural occurrence of yttrium with the heavier lanthanides (pp. 67–70); for the difficulties experienced in separating yttrium from these elements (Chapter 1); and for the marked similarities in crystal structure, solubility, and chemical properties between yttrium compounds and those of the heavier lanthanides that make yttrium a practical member of this series. Indeed, the behavior of the more abundant yttrium (Table 1.3) is considered to be so characteristic of these elements that they are referred to as *yttrium earths*. The rather marked differences observed between the chemistry of scandium and that of the lanthanides are consistent with the fact that the Sc^{3+} ion is much smaller than even the Lu^{3+} ion.

The lanthanide contraction is responsible for the small variations in properties that permit separation of the lanthanides by fractional means (pp. 75–91). In terms of crystal radius, basicity may be expected to decrease in the order

$$La^{3+} > Ce^{3+} > Pr^{3+} > Nd^{3+} > Pm^{3+} > Sm^{3+} > Eu^{3+} > Gd^{3+} > Tb^{3+} >$$

$$Dy^{3+} > Ho^{3+} > Y^{3+} > Er^{3+} > Tm^{3+} > Yb^{3+} > Lu^{3+} > Sc^{3+}$$

with the more highly charged Ce^{4+} ion being less basic than any tripositive ion. Basicity differences are reflected in the hydrolysis of ions, the solubilities of salts, the thermal decomposition of oxy salts, and the formation of complex species (Chapter 3). The lanthanide contraction may be related also to the decreasing ease of oxidation of the metals with increasing atomic number, as shown by oxidation potential (Table 2.3) and ionization energy (Table 3.1) data.

Certain of these effects· continue beyond the lanthanides. Thus, although titanium and zirconium (Periodic Group IVb) differ substantially, hafnium resembles zirconium so closely that the separation of their compounds is at least as difficult as separation of those of adjacent lanthanides. Further striking similarities are noted between niobium and tantalum (Group Vb), molybdenum and tungsten (Group VIb), and technetium and rhenium (Group VIIb). Indeed, these similarities between members of the second and third d-type transition series continue through the platinum metals to at least silver and gold. They result, of course, from the lanthanide-induced reductions in crystal radii in the third series, as indicated by the values (in Ångstrom units):

Group IVb: Ti^{4+} 0.68, Zr^{4+} 0.79, Hf^{4+} 0.78

Group Vb: V^{5+} 0.59, Nb^{5+} 0.69, Ta^{5+} 0.68

Group VIb: Cr^{6+} 0.52, Mo^{6+} 0.62, W^{6+} 0.62

Group VIIb: Mn^{7+} 0.46, Tc^{7+} 0.56, Re^{7+} 0.56

Some Direct Consequences of Electronic Configuration

The indirect consequences are largely chemical; the direct ones substantially physical. Although the most obvious of the latter, the emission spectra, are of extreme importance, we can do no more in this treatment than indicate their utility in measuring purity. On the other hand, the $4f$ electrons are directly responsible for both the magnetic and light absorption properties of the cationic species, and these properties are more amenable to interpretation. Both such characteristics are related to the presence of unpaired electrons. For this reason, the preferential single occupancy of the seven $4f$ orbitals before pairing can occur (p. 13) is of importance.

Magnetic Characteristics. The major magnetic properties of chemical substances result from the fact that each moving electron is itself a micromagnet. Since an electron has both *spin* and *orbital* motion, it may contribute to magnetic behavior in two ways. The observed magnetic properties of a substance then represent the combined contributions of all of the electrons present. When a substance is placed in a magnetic field, it is observed to align itself either in opposition to the field (*diamagnetic behavior*) or parallel to the field (*paramagnetic behavior*). Diamagnetism results when pairing of all electrons nullifies their individual contributions. The ions Y^{3+}, La^{3+}, Lu^{3+}, Yb^{2+}, and Ce^{4+} are diamagnetic. Paramagnetism results when unpaired electrons are present to prevent such compensation. All of the other lanthanide ions are paramagnetic.

Magnetic character is described in terms of the molar magnetic susceptibility, χ_M. Molar diamagnetic susceptibility has a magnitude of ca. 10^{-6} c.g.s. units; molar paramagnetic susceptibility a magnitude in the range 10^{-3} to 10^{-2} c.g.s. units. The molar susceptibility is related empirically to the Kelvin temperature, T, by the Langevin expression

$$\chi_M = \mathcal{N}\mu_B{}^2/3kT \tag{2.1}$$

where $\mathcal{N}$ is Avogadro's number, k is the Boltzmann constant, and μ_B is the permanent magnetic moment of the species in question. Each paramagnetic substance has its own characteristic permanent magnetic moment (expressed in Bohr magnetons). The underlying diamagnetism of a paramagnetic species is normally so small that it can be neglected unless the greatest accuracy is required. Contrary to what one might expect on these bases, however, the most strongly paramagnetic species is not the Gd^{3+} ion with seven unpaired $4f$ electrons (Table 2.6). Rather, the ions Dy^{3+} and Ho^{3+} have

TABLE 2.6. Permanent Magnetic Moments of Tripositive Cations

Ion	Unpaired electrons	μ_B, Bohr magnetons		
		Theoretical (Van Vleck)	Observed ($Ln_2(SO_4)_3 \cdot 8H_2O$)	Observed ($Ln(C_5H_5)_3$)
La^{3+}	0	0	*	0
Ce^{3+}	1	2.56	—	2.46
Pr^{3+}	2	3.62	3.47	3.61
Nd^{3+}	3	3.68	3.52	3.63
Pm^{3+}	4	2.83	—	—
Sm^{3+}	5	1.55–1.65	1.58	1.54
Eu^{3+}	6	3.40–3.51	3.54	—
Gd^{3+}	7	7.94	7.9	7.98
Tb^{3+}	6	9.7	9.6	—
Dy^{3+}	5	10.6	10.3	10.0
Ho^{3+}	4	10.6	10.4	—
Er^{3+}	3	9.6	9.4	9.45
Tm^{3+}	2	7.6	7.0	—
Yb^{3+}	1	4.5	4.3	4.00
Lu^{3+}	0	0	—	—
Y^{3+}	0	0	0	

* Does not give such a salt.

maximum permanent moment, and a second, but less pronounced, maximum characterizes the Nd^{3+} ion.

The American physicist J. H. Van Vleck has shown that although Eq. 2.1 is generally valid, the properties of paramagnetic substances can be better described by the relationship

$$\chi_M = N\bar{\mu}_B^2/3kT + N\bar{\alpha} \qquad (2.2)$$

where $\bar{\mu}_B$ is a low-frequency part of the magnetic moment and $\bar{\alpha}$ is a combination high-frequency component and diamagnetic contribution. Because the $4f$ electrons are shielded, both their orbital and spin motions contribute, and the observed permanent moment results from appropriate coupling of these components. Its magnitude is determined by the magnitudes of separation between the energy levels so produced and the term kT. In practice, it is found that only with the Gd^{3+} ion are these separations sufficiently small in comparison with kT to allow one to neglect the last term in Eq. 2.2. For all other tripositive ions except Sm^{3+} and Eu^{3+}, they are large enough so that both terms must be considered. For the ions Sm^{3+} and Eu^{3+}, they are of about the same order of magnitude as kT, and again both terms must be considered but in a different way. The net result is that the permanent magnetic moment of only the Gd^{3+} ion depends directly upon the number of un-paired electrons or, most specifically, upon electron spin. In all other cases, the value observed reflects a combination of spin and orbital effects. The validity of these considerations is shown by the agreement between theoretically calculated and experimentally measured values (Table 2.6).

It is pertinent to recall that the magnetic moments of the cations of the first d-type transition series are determined largely by the number of unpaired d electrons. Inasmuch as these electrons also participate in bond formation, their orbital contributions are quenched by the bonded groups, and ob-served moment is only a function of electron spin. Thus, the magnetic moments of such ions are markedly affected by com-plexing ligands. It is observed, however, that complexing groups—or, indeed, anions of any type—have little effect upon the magnetic moments of the lanthanide ions, as long as the resulting structure is such that each paramagnetic ion can remain far enough from the others to behave independently (i.e., a magnetically dilute structure). Thus, as a result of shielding, the f orbitals differ somewhat from the d orbitals.

The electronic configurations suggested for the nontriposi-tive species (Table 2.2) are in agreement with magnetic data. Thus, cerium(IV) and ytterbium(II) are diamagnetic, corre-sponding to $4f^0$ and $4f^{14}$ configurations; samarium(II) and europium(III) are magnetically similar (both $4f^6$); and euro-pium(II) gives values very nearly the same as those for gadolinium(III) (both $4f^7$).

Color and Light Absorption. The striking colors characteristic of crystalline salts of a number of the tripositive ions
persist in aqueous and nonaqueous solutions and are unaffected by alteration of the anion present or addition of colorless complexing groups. They are apparently characteristic of
the cations themselves. Interestingly, the colors of the ions
from La^{3+} through Gd^{3+} repeat themselves, at least qualitatively, from Lu^{3+} back through Gd^{3+} (Table 2.7). It is tempt-

TABLE 2.7. Color Sequence for Tripositive Cations

Ion	Unpaired electrons	Color	Unpaired electrons	Ion
La^{3+}	0	Colorless	0	Lu^{3+}
Ce^{3+}	1	Colorless	1	Yb^{3+}
Pr^{3+}	2	Green	2	Tm^{3+}
Nd^{3+}	3	Reddish	3	Er^{3+}
Pm^{3+}	4	Pink; yellow	4	Ho^{3+}
Sm^{3+}	5	Yellow	5	Dy^{3+}
Eu^{3+}	6	Pale pink (?)	6	Tb^{3+}
Gd^{3+}	7	Colorless	7	Gd^{3+}

ing to conclude, then, that a given color is related to a given
number of unpaired electrons, but the divergence in color
between the tripositive species and isoelectronic nontripositive
ions (Table 2.8) suggests that the situation is somewhat more
complex. Furthermore, the ions Ce^{3+}, Gd^{3+}, and Yb^{3+}, all of
which contain unpaired electrons, are colorless.

TABLE 2.8. Colors of Isoelectronic Ions

Tripositive Ion	Color	Unpaired electrons	Color	Nontripositive Ion
La^{3+}	Colorless	0	Orange-red	Ce^{4+}
Eu^{3+}	Pale pink	6	Reddish	Sm^{2+}
Gd^{3+}	Colorless	7	Straw yellow	Eu^{2+}
Lu^{3+}	Colorless	0	Green	Yb^{2+}

Inasmuch as color has no quantitative significance, it is more fundamental to measure the amounts of light of different wavelengths absorbed by each species. This is reasonable since the color one sees is the result of absorption of light of certain wavelengths and transmission of light of other wavelengths. With such measurements, it is observed that all the tripositive ions except Y^{3+}, La^{3+}, and Lu^{3+} absorb somewhere in the wavelength range 2000–10000 Å.[*] The colored ions absorb in the visible region, and on occasion in the ultraviolet. The colorless species absorb either in the ultraviolet (Ce^{3+}, Gd^{3+}) or the infrared (Yb^{3+}). The dipositive ions absorb strongly in the ultraviolet. The only tetrapositive ion stable in aqueous solution, the Ce^{4+} ion, absorbs in the blue and ultraviolet regions.

The absorption spectrum of each of the tripositive ions (except Ce^{3+} and Yb^{3+}) contains several very sharply defined bands, as indicated by the typical spectra in Fig. 2.3 and the data in Table 2.9. These bands, although not intense, peak at wavelengths that can often be measured to an Ångstrom unit

TABLE 2.9. Principal Absorption Bands

Ion	Wavelength, Å.	Ion	Wavelength, Å.
La^{3+}	None	Tb^{3+}	3694, 3780, 4875
Ce^{3+}	2105, 2220, 2380, 2520	Dy^{3+}	3504, 3650, 9100
Pr^{3+}	4445, 4690, 4822, 5885	Ho^{3+}	2870, 3611, 4508, 5370, 6404
Nd^{3+}	3540, 5218, 5745, 7395, 7420, 7975, 8030, 8680	Er^{3+}	3642, 3792, 4870, 5228, 6525
		Tm^{3+}	3600, 6825, 7800
Pm^{3+}	5485, 5680, 7025, 7355	Yb^{3+}	9750
Sm^{3+}	3625, 3745, 4020	Lu^{3+}	None
Eu^{3+}	3755, 3941		
Gd^{3+}	2729, 2733, 2754, 2756	Y^{3+}	None

[*] The eye is sensitive to radiation in the region 4000–7000 Å. This is the *visible* region. The region below 4000 Å. is the *ultraviolet;* that above 7000 Å. the *infrared.* The energy associated with radiation increases as wavelength decreases.

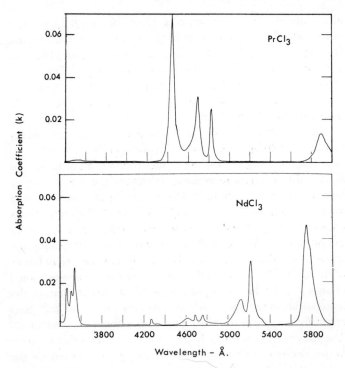

Fig. 2.3. Portions of absorption spectra of aqueous $PrCl_3$ and $NdCl_3$ solutions. (Redrawn from Moeller, T., and Brantley, J. C., *Anal. Chem.* **22,** 433 (1950).)

or less. As such, they resemble the lines of emission spectra more closely than the broad absorption bands of *d*-type transition metal ions (e.g., Ti^{3+}, Ni^{2+}, Pt^{4+}). Indeed, such line-like absorption spectra are characteristic of no other ionic species except the related actinides. These bands are even more sharply defined for crystalline solids than for solutions. Decreasing the temperature and adding strongly complexing ligands also have a sharpening effect. However, neither changing from solution to solid nor introducing complexing groups alters the general spectrum of a given ion or changes more than slightly the wavelengths of the sharp absorption bands. In contrast, the absorption bands of the Ce^{3+} and Yb^{3+} ions are broad and are altered by complexing groups. The broad, intense ultraviolet absorption bands of the Sm^{2+} and Eu^{2+} ions have superimposed upon them weaker, line-like bands. Those of the Yb^{2+} ion do not.

Absorption bands, like emission lines, reflect the energy changes resulting from transitions from one level to another. Inasmuch as the ground-state configuration of all of these ions is $4f^n$, this configuration must represent the lowest energy level for such transitions. The higher level may be either another configuration such as $4f^{n-1}5d^1$ or $4f^{n-1}5g^1$ or a similar configuration, $4f^{n'}$, where some small differences in energy are permitted. Although the details are somewhat beyond the scope of this discussion, it can be shown that the broad bands of the Ce^{3+}, Yb^{3+}, and Ln^{2+} ions result from configurational changes of the first type, whereas the weak but sharply defined bands of the other Ln^{3+} ions and the Sm^{2+} and Eu^{2+} ions result from electronic transitions within the $4f$ arrangement. The latter are possible only because of the disturbing effects of the electrical fields (so-called *crystal fields*) imposed by the anions that surround these cations. Such transitions prove to be impossible with $4f^1$ (Ce^{3+}), $4f^{13}$ (Yb^{3+}), or $4f^{14}$ (Yb^{2+}) configurations. Inasmuch as the $4f$ electrons are so well shielded, it is not surprising that neither the nature nor the environment of the compound being studied has much effect upon the sharply defined bands.

The almost unique absorptions associated with the f electrons make certain of the ions of the lanthanides particularly useful in light filters. Glass containing neodymium and praseodymium ions (so-called didymium glass) absorbs yellow sodium light so specifically and so strongly that it is used extensively in glass blowers' goggles. Indeed, standard filters that take advantage of the sharpness of the absorption bands are used uniformly for wavelength calibration in optical devices. The absorption spectra of the tripositive ions are also used extensively for both the qualitative detection and the quantitative determination of the lanthanides in mixtures (p. 74).

Again, Recapitulation—and Then?

The ease and logic with which we have been able to answer many of the questions raised in Chapter 1 may suggest to us that a complete understanding of the chemistry of the lanthanides should result from mere consideration of their electronic configurations. Certainly, we have in this way accounted for many early experimental observations that would otherwise remain as confusing as they were when they were first recorded. Although in principle an extension of these considerations should give us this understanding, our enthusiasm for the purely theoretical approach must certainly be tempered by the fact that we still do not have sufficient factual information in mind to judge its validity and scope. It is essential, therefore, for us to summarize in some detail the chemical behaviors of the metals and their ions by bringing together in the next chapter in a logical manner the wealth of data accumulated during a century and a half of experimental observation.

When we do this, we shall find that there are certain facts, relating in particular to yttrium chemistry but also encompassing that of the heavier members of the series, that are unexplained by the approach we have developed. The imperfections and weaknesses of these concepts may help convince us of the danger of accepting any theoretical approach without first examining it in the light of *all* pertinent factual information. If the theory is fundamentally sound, it can by slight alteration accommodate apparent exceptions; if it is unsound it cannot accommodate these and thus must be rejected. Fortunately, the former applies to the lanthanides.

Selected Readings

Asprey, L. B., and Cunningham, B. B., "Progress in Inorganic Chemistry," F. A. Cotton, Ed., Vol. II, pp. 267–86, Interscience Publishers, New York, 1960. (Oxidation states).

Moeller, T., "The Rare Earths," F. H. Spedding and A. H. Daane, Eds. ch. 2, John Wiley & Sons, New York, 1961. (Electronic configuration and general properties.)

Moeller, T., and Kremers, H. E., *Chem. Rev.* **37,** 98–159 (1945). (Size relationships and basicity.)

Selwood, P. W., "Magnetochemistry," 2nd ed., pp. 140–57, Interscience Publishers, New York, 1956. (Magnetic properties.)

Yost, D. M., Russell, H., Jr., and Garner, C. S., "The Rare-Earth Elements and Their Compounds," chs. 1–3, John Wiley & Sons, New York, 1947. (Electronic configurations, oxidation states, magnetic properties, absorption spectra.)

chapter three

THE OXIDATION STATES—
A COMBINATION OF THE
COMMONPLACE
AND THE UNUSUAL

It is now appropriate that we supplement the small amount of chemical information already presented, implement the approaches outlined in Chapter 2, and add to our fund of knowledge by discussing in some detail the general chemistry of the lanthanides. This is conveniently done in terms of the several oxidation states already mentioned.

Oxidation State Zero—The Metals

Yttrium and the elemental lanthanides are all metals, as might be expected from their electronic configurations (Table 2.1), their large atomic radii (Table 2.4), and their position in the Periodic Table. As metals of commerce and for laboratory usage, most of them are comparative newcomers. This stems from a combination of unavailability of pure compounds from which they can be prepared and of difficulty of preparation. The successful solution of these problems in the years since around 1950 is described in detail in subsequent sections (pp. 41–43, 80–92).

Physical Characteristics. Important physical constants supplementing those already given (Tables 2.3 and 2.4) are listed in Table 3.1. Many of these values are more meaningful when they are compared with those for more familiar elements, as presented in Table 3.2. The wide ranges of density, melting point, boiling point, and cross section for thermal (slow) neutron capture encompassed by these elements are apparent. As is characteristic of any periodic family, density increases in general with atomic weight. The exceptions at europium and ytterbium probably reflect differences in crystal structure (Table 3.1). In fusibility and volatility, europium and ytterbium resemble calcium more closely than they do the neighboring lanthanides. This may again suggest a difference in inherent oxidation state (p. 22), for the melting point and boiling point are measures of the strength of bonding in the solid and liquid states, respectively.

Inasmuch as neutron absorption is a nuclear property, it bears no direct relationship to atomic number. Cerium compares with our weaker neutron absorbers (Table 3.2), but samarium, europium, and gadolinium are more effective than boron or cadmium, the substances normally used in neutron-control devices (p. 94). Europium is of particular interest because its isotopes undergo series of n,γ reactions, each of which gives a europium isotope of large absorption cross section.[*]

The metals are soft, malleable, and ductile. When freshly

---

[*] In an n,γ reaction, a nucleus absorbs a neutron, thereby undergoing an increase in mass, and emits *gamma* (very short wavelength) radiation. There is no change in nuclear charge.

TABLE 3.1. Numerical Constants for the Elements

Symbol	Atomic weight ($^{12}C = 12.0000$)	Density,* g./cm.³	Ionization energy,[†] e.v./g. atom	Melting point, °C.	Boiling point (approx.), °C.	Cross section for thermal neutron capture,[‡] barns/atom
Sc	44.956	2.992	6.56	1539	2727	24
Y	88.905	4.478	6.6	1509	2927	1.31
La	138.91	6.174	5.61	920	3469	9.3
Ce	140.12	6.771	6.91	795	3468	0.73
Pr	140.907	6.782	5.76	935	3127	11.6
Nd	144.24	7.004	6.31	1024	3027	46
Pm	(147)	—	—	—	—	—
Sm	150.35	7.536	5.6	1072	1900	5600
Eu	151.96	5.259	5.67	826	1439	4300
Gd	157.25	7.895	6.16	1312	3000	46000
Tb	158.924	8.272	6.74	1356	2800	46
Dy	162.50	8.536	6.82	1407	2600	950
Ho	164.930	8.803	—	1461	2600	65
Er	167.26	9.051	—	1497	2900	173
Tm	168.934	9.332	—	1545	1727	127
Yb	173.04	6.977	6.2	824	1427	37
Lu	174.97	9.842	5.0	1652	3327	115

* For stable modification at room temperature—all hexagonal close-packed except Sm (rhombohedral), Eu (body-centered cubic), Yb (face-centered cubic).

[†] For one electron.

[‡] For neutrons of velocity 2200 m./sec. Natural isotopic mixtures.

TABLE 3.2. Some Numerical Constants* for Comparison

Symbol	Density g./cm.³	Symbol	Melting point, °C	Symbol	Boiling point (approx.), °C	Symbol	Neutron capture, barns/atom
Al	2.7	Sr	770	K	1400	Zr	0.18
Ba	3.5	As	814	Cd	1413	Rb	0.73
Ti	4.54	Ca	851	Sb	1440	Sr	1.21
Ge	5.32	Ge	936	Ca	1482	Pt	8.8
V	6.11	Ag	960.5	Te	1814	Se	12.3
Zr	6.45	Au	1063	In	2075	Ta	21
Sb	6.68	Cu	1083	Mn	2097	Cs	29
Zn	7.13	Be	1284	Cr	2199	Co	37
Mn	7.44	Ni	1452	Cu	2595	Ag	63
Fe	7.87	Co	1493	Ge	2700	Hf	105
Nb	8.57	Fe	1535	Ni	2900	Rh	156
Cd	8.65	Pd	1552	Au	2966	In	196
Cu	8.94	Ti	1668	Fe	3000	B	755
Bi	9.08			Co	3100	Cd	2450
				Ti	3260		
				Zr	3580		

* Data from Hampel, C. A., "Rare Metals Handbook," 2nd ed., ch. 35, Reinhold Publishing Corp., New York, 1961.

cut, they have a silvery luster. In electrical conductivity, they cover the same range that cesium and mercury do. Except for yttrium, which is only mildly so, the metals are appreciably paramagnetic (p. 26). Terbium is very strongly paramagnetic, and gadolinium is unique in being ferromagnetic* up to 16°C.

Chemical Characteristics. The oxidation potentials for the couples Ln^0–Ln^{III} in acidic solution (Table 2.3) suggest that these metals are comparable to magnesium in electropositive character and ease of oxidation. The same is true under alkaline conditions, although the potential data (La, ca. 2.90 v., and Lu, ca. 2.72 v.; vs. Mg, 2.69 v.) are even less well established. Inasmuch as these potentials measure displacement of equilibria of the types[†]

$$Ln(s) + xH_2O \rightleftharpoons Ln(H_2O)_x^{3+} + 3e^- \quad \text{(acidic medium)}$$

and

$$Ln(s) + 3OH^- \rightleftharpoons Ln(OH)_3(s) + 3e^- \quad \text{(alkaline medium)}$$

they indicate ease of oxidation under aqueous conditions. That the metals are strong reducing agents under these conditions follows from the large amounts of energy released in the hydration or hydrolysis of their gaseous tripositive ions as compared with the smaller quantities of energy needed to form these ions (p. 18). We may wonder, therefore, whether or not comparable ease of oxidation is noted in the absence of

---

* Ferromagnetism ($\chi_M = \infty$) differs from paramagnetism in that it results from the parallel orientation of molecular magnets over microscopic regions of a crystalline solid. A ferromagnetic substance becomes paramagnetic when the temperature is raised above a characteristic critical value (the Curie temperature or point). Typical Curie points are: Gd, 16°C.; Dy, −168°C. Common ferromagnetic materials include iron and certain of its alloys (especially with cobalt and nickel).

† Inasmuch as x is not known with certainty, we may also formulate these ions Ln^{3+}(aq), as was done in Table 2.3.

water. It is observed that although reactions under these conditions are strongly exothermic, they are normally slow at room temperature and take place rapidly and vigorously only when the temperature is raised.

Reactions of the metals with typical reagents are summarized in Table 3.3. The large concentration of hydronium ion in dilute aqueous acids promotes vigorous oxidation to the tripositive cation in each instance. Water, with its reduced hydronium ion content, reacts more slowly at room temperature to give the insoluble hydrous oxide or hydroxide, but reasonably rapidly at elevated temperatures. Europium is attacked much more rapidly than the other metals, forming first the soluble, yellowish $Eu(OH)_2 \cdot H_2O$ (compare alkaline

TABLE 3.3. Typical Chemical Reactions of the Elemental Lanthanides

Reagent(s)	Product(s)	Conditions
X_2 ($= F_2, Cl_2, Br_2, I_2$)	LnX_3	Slow at room temperature; burn above 200°C.
O_2	Ln_2O_3	Slow at room temperature; burn above 150–180°C.
S	Ln_2S_3	At boiling point of sulfur
N_2	LnN	Above 1000°C.
C	LnC_2, Ln_2C_3 (also LnC, Ln_2C, Ln_3C, Ln_4C)	At high temperature
B	LnB_4, LnB_6	At high temperature
H_2	LnH_2, LnH_3	Rapid above 300°C.
H^+ (dil. HCl, H_2SO_4, $HClO_4$, $HC_2H_3O_2$, etc.)	$Ln^{3+} + H_2$	Rapid at room temperature
H_2O	Ln_2O_3 or $Ln(OH)_3 + H_2$	Slow at room temperature; more rapid at higher temperature
$H_2O + O_2$	Ln_2O_3 or $Ln(OH)_3$	Rapid with Eu; slower with others
Metal oxides	Metal	At high temperatures (except CaO, MgO, Ln_2O_3 in general)

earth metals) and then hydrous Eu_2O_3. Dry oxygen (air) attacks the pure metals very slowly at room temperature, but at higher temperatures the metals ignite and burn. Moist air attacks europium very rapidly, and lanthanum, cerium, praseodymium, and neodymium quite rapidly. The resulting hydrous oxide is always so voluminous that any protective oxide coating is ruptured, and a new metal surface is continually exposed. The impure metals and alloys rich in cerium (e.g., mischmetal, p. 92) are pyrophoric. Other reactions require no additional comment.

Europium and ytterbium, like the alkaline earth and alkali metals, dissolve in liquid ammonia to yield the dark blue, strongly reducing solutions that are believed to contain the ammonated electron, $e(NH_3)_y^-$. This behavior emphasizes the ease with which these metals lose electrons.

Preparation. The ease of oxidation of the metals suggests that reduction of ions to the metallic state is difficult. In aqueous systems, neither electrolytic nor chemical reduction is effective; rather, hydrogen is the preferential reduction product. Decrease in ease of oxidation upon alloying with mercury, however, permits amalgam formation when buffered acetic acid solutions are treated with sodium amalgam or when alkaline citrate solutions are electrolyzed with a lithium-amalgam cathode. Electrolysis or displacement is effective in nonaqueous media (e.g., in alcohols) only if amalgams can result. Thermal decomposition of such amalgams gives the finely divided metals, but complete removal of mercury is difficult. Under any circumstance, europium, ytterbium, and samarium (and in this order) give amalgams most readily.

Two more generally successful reduction systems involve electrolysis of molten halides and metallothermic treatment of anhydrous salts. Electrolysis is complicated both by the high melting points of the useful anhydrous salts (Table 3.4) and by the reactivity of the liberated metals with gases and cell refractories. Lower temperatures are achieved with lower-melting mixtures of salts. Thus pure cerium is obtained by electrolyzing molten CeF_3–LiF–BaF_2 at temperatures near the melting point of that metal and adding cerium(IV) oxide to replenish the bath, and yttrium is obtained in high purity from a KCl–YCl_3 melt.

Metallothermic reduction of the anhydrous fluorides with calcium in tantalum apparatus at ca. 800–1000°C., as developed at Iowa State University by A. H. Daane, H. A. Wilhelm, and F. H. Spedding,

$$2LnF_3 + 3Ca \rightarrow 2Ln + 3CaF_2$$

is generally considered more convenient. Alternative but comparable procedures use the anhydrous chlorides and magnesium, lithium, or sodium, but the fluorides are preferred

TABLE 3.4. Melting Points[*] of Some Typical Anhydrous Lanthanide(III) Compounds

Cation	Melting point, °C.			
	Fluoride	Chloride	Bromide	Iodide
Sc^{3+}	1515	960	960	945
Y^{3+}	1152	700	904	1000
La^{3+}	1493	852	783	761
Ce^{3+}	1430	802	732	752
Pr^{3+}	1395	776	693	733
Nd^{3+}	1374	760	684	775
Pm^{3+}	—	—	—	—
Sm^{3+}	1306	678	664	816–824
Eu^{3+}	1276	623	(702)	(877)
Gd^{3+}	1231	609	765	926
Tb^{3+}	1172	588	(827)	952
Dy^{3+}	1154	654	881	955
Ho^{3+}	1143	718	914	1010
Er^{3+}	1140	774	950	1020
Tm^{3+}	1158	821	(952)	1015
Yb^{3+}	1157	854	940	(1027)
Lu^{3+}	1182	892	(957)	1045

[*] Estimated values in parentheses.

because they are not hygroscopic. The trifluorides of samarium, europium, and ytterbium are reduced only to the difluorides. However, the fact that these metals are more volatile than lanthanum permits their preparation *in vacuo* from the oxides, as

$$Ln_2O_3 + 2La \rightarrow La_2O_3 + 2Ln(g)$$

The metals are best purified by distillation in tantalum apparatus with a vacuum of at least 10^{-5}mm. of Hg.

Oxidation State +2—A So-Called "Anomalous" State

Although C. Matignon and E. Cazes obtained samarium(II) chloride in 1906 by reducing the trichloride at elevated temperatures with hydrogen, ammonia, or aluminum, and G. Urbain and F. Bourion prepared europium(II) chloride in 1911 by a comparable reduction involving hydrogen, the true significance and possible utility of these observations were not realized until about 1930. In 1929, W. Klemm and W. Schuth obtained ytterbium(II) chloride by hydrogen reduction, and the following year, L. F. Yntema and R. Ball, working in the laboratory of the University of Illinois, obtained the Eu^{2+} and Yb^{2+} ions in aqueous solution by electrolytic reduction. Subsequent work has shown that a number of other dipositive species can be prepared (Table 2.2). Proposals that all of the lanthanides can be dipositive, however, lack complete experimental verification.

Chemical Stability and Stabilization. It is convenient to discuss samarium(II), europium(II), and ytterbium(II) separately because only these dipositive species exist in aqueous solution and form series of compounds. Standard oxidation potential data (Table 2.3) indicate that in aqueous solution these three cations are all strong reducing agents, with reducing strength decreasing as

$$Sm^{2+} >> Yb^{2+} >> Eu^{2+}$$

Thus the Eu^{2+} ion lies between elemental iron and cadmium, the Yb^{2+} ion just below elemental manganese, and the Sm^{2+} ion just below elemental aluminum. Both the Sm^{2+} and Yb^{2+} ions are rapidly oxidized by hydronium ion

$$2Ln^{2+} + 2H_3O^+ \longrightarrow 2Ln^{3+} + 2H_2O + H_2(g)$$

but the Eu^{2+} ion is oxidized only very slowly. In the presence of oxygen, all ions are oxidized rapidly

$$4Ln^{2+} + 4H_3O^+ + O_2 \longrightarrow 4Ln^{3+} + 6H_2O$$

At reduced acidity, either reaction path may give difficultly soluble basic salts, LnOX. The general instability of the dipositive species with respect to oxidation has been discussed in Chapter 2 (pp. 18, 19).

Although some stabilization with respect to oxidation may be expected in less strongly solvating media (e.g., the alcohols), it is best achieved by including these ions in solid compounds. Hydrated water-soluble samarium(II) and ytterbium(II) salts are oxidized by their water, but those of europium(II), particularly the chloride $EuCl_2 \cdot 2H_2O$, are comparatively stable. Water-insoluble compounds (e.g., the sulfates, carbonates, fluorides) resist oxidation even in the presence of water. The sulfates are most useful for recovery and preservation of these ions. More extensive stabilization is noted when the ions are trapped in an inert solid matrix (e.g., EuO in SrO, Ln^{2+} in silicate glasses, LnF_2 in LnF_3).

The other dipositive species are known only as solid halides. All are immediately oxidized upon contact with water. The observed isomorphism between the compounds TmI_2 and YbI_2 suggests that the ion Tm^{2+} exists. However, some of the other dihalides show the metallic properties associated with "free" electrons and are perhaps better formulated as $Ln^{3+}(e^-)(X^-)_2$.

General Physical and Chemical Properties. Properties of the Sm^{2+}, Eu^{2+}, and Yb^{2+} ions related to electronic configuration have been discussed in Chapter 2. As the crystal radii (Table 2.4) suggest and as we imply in previous discussions, there are striking similarities in solubility and crystal structure between compounds of these ions and those of the alkaline earth metal ions (especially Sr^{2+} and Ba^{2+}). For this reason, the Sr^{2+} and Ba^{2+} ions are commonly used to carry the dipositive lanthanides in separations (p. 92). Cases in point include both the sulfates (above) and the chloride $EuCl_2 \cdot 2H_2O$. The latter, like its barium analog, is difficultly soluble in concentrated hydrochloric acid.

The dipositive fluorides are all isomorphous and have the cubic fluorite (CaF_2) structure (p. 64). Anhydrous samarium(II) chloride is isostructural with the strontium and barium compounds, but europium(II) and ytterbium(II) chlorides are not. Of the dipositive bromides, only the ytterbium compound is not isostructural with strontium bromide. None of the iodides is isomorphous with either strontium or barium iodide. The oxides, sulfides, selenides, and tellurides, insofar as they have been examined, have the cubic sodium chloride-type structure of their strontium and barium analogs. The carbonates are isomorphous with barium carbonate. Only samarium(II) and europium(II) sulfates have the barium sulfate structure. It is apparent that some structures can better tolerate small variations in crystal radii than others.

Although it is known that one or two europium(II) amine-polycarboxylate complex ions (p. 55) have essentially the same solution stability as their strontium counterparts, detailed information on complex species is lacking.

Preparation. General methods of obtaining the dipositive lanthanides include

1. *Reduction of anhydrous compounds at elevated temperatures.* Typical procedures include reduction of the anhydrous fluo-

rides or chlorides as previously described (p. 43) and reduction of fused trihalides (e.g., NdX_3, TmI_3) or of oxides (e.g., Eu_2O_3, Sm_2O_3) with the corresponding metal.

2. *Chemical reduction in solution.*   Amalgamated zinc (e.g., as a Jones reductor) reduces europium(III) quantitatively to europium(II), but samarium(III) and ytterbium(III) are unaffected. The observation that magnesium reduces samarium(III) chloride to insoluble samarium(II) chloride in anhydrous ethanol suggests that a variety of procedures involving nonaqueous systems may be feasible.

3. *Electrolytic reduction in solution.*   Both aqueous europium(III) and ytterbium(III) solutions yield the dipositive ions at a mercury cathode (p. 43), but the samarium(II) ion is too strongly reducing to be so prepared.

4. *Thermal decomposition of anhydrous iodides.*   Ease of reduction at elevated temperatures as

$$2LnX_3(s) \longrightarrow 2LnX_2(s) + X_2(g)$$

increases in the series Sm^{3+}–Yb^{3+}–Eu^{3+} and Cl^-–Br^-–I^-.

5. *Chemical oxidation.*   Samarium, europium, and ytterbium amalgams, when treated with acid, apparently give the dipositive ions as intermediate oxidation products.   Mercury(II) iodide oxidizes elemental thulium to the diiodide.

Oxidation State +3—The "Characteristic" State

It is apparent from previous discussions (Chapters 1 and 2) that the properties of this state very largely determine the chemistry of the lanthanides. For completeness, however, it is necessary to consider in more detail the properties of specific compounds and complex ion formation.   These are important both to our understanding of the nature of bonding and to our appreciation of the practical chemistry discussed in Chapter 4.

Properties—Some Specific and General Considerations. The tripositive species are found in generally crystalline compounds containing essentially all known anionic species. Where these anions can be decomposed thermally (e.g., $OH^-, CO_3^{2-}, SO_4^{2-}, C_2O_4^{2-}, NO_3^-$), the corresponding compounds are converted to basic derivatives and ultimately to oxides when heated. Hydrated salts, as a consequence of hydrolysis at elevated temperatures, often give similar products. Anhydrous compounds containing thermally stable anions (e.g., O^{2-}, F^-, Cl^-, Br^-, PO_4^{3-}) melt without decomposition. Both their high melting points (e.g., Table 3.4) and excellent electrical conductivities in the fused state indicate a high degree of ionic bonding. Available crystal structure data show the presence of Ln^{3+} ions.

Conductance, transference number,[*] and activity coefficient[†] data, of which those given for the chlorides in Table 3.5 are typical, indicate that salts containing weakly basic anions (e.g., Cl^-, Br^-, I^-, NO_3^-, ClO_4^-) are strong electrolytes in aqueous solution. Indeed, such solutions are often used as standards of comparison for electrolyte behavior since solutions derived from other tripositive species (e.g., Cr^{3+}, Fe^{3+}, Al^{3+}, In^{3+}) are those of weaker electrolytes as a consequence of enhanced covalence, solvation, and complex ion formation. The influence of the lanthanide contraction is apparent in the general decrease in ionic character from lanthanum to lutetium.

A similar trend is noted in the slight increase in degree of

---

[*] The transference number of an ion is the fraction of the total current carried by that ion in a conductance experiment.

[†] The activity coefficient of an ion is the correction factor γ needed to convert observed molality (m) to effective (thermodynamic) concentration or activity (a) in the relationship $a = \gamma m$. For a salt M_xA_y, the mean activity coefficient ($\gamma_\pm$) is equal to $\gamma_+^x \gamma_-^y$.

TABLE 3.5. Some Physical Properties of Aqueous $LnCl_3$ Solutions at 25° C.[*]

Ion	Normality	Equivalent conductance, mho/cm.	Normality	Transference number of Ln^{3+}	Molality	Mean activity coefficient, $\gamma_\pm$
La^{3+}	0.0010	137.4	—	—	0.00125	0.7661
	0.0100	122.1	0.00903	0.4629	0.01247	0.5318
	0.1000	99.0	0.0933	0.4389	—	—
Gd^{3+}	0.0010	134.9	—	—	0.00171	0.7728
	0.0100	120.2	0.0117	0.4602	0.0171	0.5345
	0.1000	98.4	0.1051	0.4315	—	—
Yb^{3+}	0.0010	132.8	—	—	0.00114	0.7732
	0.0100	118.1	0.0104	0.4495	0.01144	0.5385
	0.1000	96.4	0.1038	0.4224	—	—

[*] Adapted from Spedding, F. H., et al., J. Am. Chem. Soc., **74**, 2055, 2778, 2781, 4751 (1952); **76**, 879 (1954).

hydrolysis in solution from the La^{3+} ion to the Lu^{3+} ion. However, unlike the more common tripositive ions, these cations are never extensively hydrolyzed. Thus solutions containing weakly basic anions are only mildly acidic. Strongly basic anions (e.g., CN^-, S^{2-}, NO_2^-, OCN^-, N_3^-) are themselves so strongly hydrolyzed to hydroxyl ion that they precipitate basic salts or hydrous oxides. Under such circumstances, ease of precipitation decreases from the Lu^{3+} ion to the La^{3+} ion.

We see in these observations indications of the basicity order previously mentioned (p. 24). The yttrium ion usually occupies the position among the heavy lanthanides that its crystal radius suggests (see p. 20).

We have discussed the ease of formation of the tripositive ions in aqueous solution in terms of oxidation potential data (pp. 18, 19). The ease of formation and, therefore, the thermal stability of typical solid compounds containing these ions are indicated by the thermodynamic data in Table 3.6.* That these values are uniformly larger than those for comparable aluminum compounds is undoubtedly again an indication of increased ionic character. The effects of the lanthanide contraction are also apparent.

As may be expected from the crystal radii (Table 2.4), there are many cases of isomorphism. These include a num-

---

* The standard heat of formation, $\Delta H°$, is the energy associated with the formation at 25°C. of the compound from its elements. It is related to the standard free energy of formation, $\Delta F°$, and the standard entropy of formation, $\Delta S°$, by the relationship

$$\Delta H° = \Delta F° - T\Delta S°$$

The strength of a bond is measured by the magnitude of $\Delta H°$, the tendency for a reaction to take place as written by the magnitude of $\Delta F°$, and the alteration in the randomness of the system by the magnitude of $\Delta S°$. *Negative* quantities signify energy release. All spontaneous reactions have *negative* $\Delta F°$ values.

ber (but not all) of the individual halides; the oxides (within each of the three crystal types, p. 62); the hydrated sulfates, $Ln_2(SO_4)_3 \cdot 8H_2O$; the bromates, $Ln(BrO_3)_3 \cdot 9H_2O$; the many double nitrates, $2Ln(NO_3)_3 \cdot 3M^{II}(NO_3)_2 \cdot 24H_2O$ (M = Mg, Zn, Ni, Mn) and $Ln(NO_3)_3 \cdot 2NH_4NO_3 \cdot 4H_2O$; the ethyl sulfates, $Ln(C_2H_5SO_4)_3 \cdot 9H_2O$; and a host of others. Separations by fractional crystallization depend upon isomorphism. Unfortunately, the crystal structures of only a few compound types have been determined. Unlike many other tripositive ions, these cations do not form alums.

TABLE 3.6.   Some Thermodynamic Data for Formation of Typical Compounds[*]

Compound	$\Delta H°$, kcal./g. mole	$\Delta F°$, kcal./g. mole	$\Delta S°$, e.u./g. mole
La_2O_3	-428.6	(-408)	(-72)
Gd_2O_3	-434.0	(-412)	(-76)
Yb_2O_3	-433.6	(-410)	(-76)
Y_2O_3	-455.4	(-434)	(-72)
Al_2O_3	-399.9	-376.8	-12.2
$LaCl_3$	-255.9	-238	-59
$GdCl_3$	-240.1	-222	-61
$YbCl_3$	(-224)	(-206)	(-62)
YCl_3	-232.7	-215	-59
$AlCl_3$	-166.2	-152.2	-40
LaI_3	-160	(-159)	(-4)
GdI_3	-142	(-140)	(-6)
YbI_3	(-130)	(-128)	(-7)
YI_3	-137	(-136)	(-4)
AlI_3	-75.2	-75.0	$—$

[*] Data for lanthanides from Montgomery, R. L., *U. S. Bur. Mines, Rept. Invest.* **5468** (1959). Estimated values in parentheses.

Solubilities.   Water-soluble compounds include the chlorides, bromides, iodides, nitrates, acetates, perchlorates, and bromates and a number of double nitrates. Water-insoluble compounds include the fluorides, hydroxides, oxides, carbonates, chromates, phosphates, and oxalates, and indeed the salts of most di- or trinegative anions. The normal sulfates vary from very soluble to difficultly soluble.

Although it is tempting to conclude that solubility should be directly related to crystal radius, experimental observation shows that this is not the case since, depending upon the salt, solubility may decrease with decreasing radius (e.g., dimethyl phosphate, OH^-), increase with decreasing radius (e.g., double magnesium nitrates), or change irregularly (e.g., SO_4^{2-}, BrO_3^-). Such trends are shown by the data in Table 3.7. No explanation for these variations has been offered.

Very broadly, there are sufficient differences between the solubilities of many specific salts of the lighter lanthanides and those of the heavier lanthanides to justify a subdivision into so-called cerium and yttrium groups (Table 3.8). This is

TABLE 3.7. Solubilities of Typical Salts in Water

	Solubility, g./100 g. H_2O			
Cation	$Ln_2(SO_4)_3 \cdot$ $8H_2O$ $(20°C.)$	$Ln(BrO_3)_3 \cdot$ $9H_2O$ $(25°C.)$	$Ln[(CH_3)_2PO_4]_3 \cdot$ nH_2O $(25°C.)$	$LnCl_3 \cdot$ $6H_2O$ $(20°C.)$
Y^{3+}	9.76	—	2.8	217.0
La^{3+}	—	462.1	103.7	—
Ce^{3+}	9.43*	—	79.6	—
Pr^{3+}	12.74	196.1	64.1	—
Nd^{3+}	7.00	151.3	56.1	243.0
Pm^{3+}	—	—	—	—
Sm^{3+}	2.67	117.3	35.2	218.4
Eu^{3+}	2.56	—	—	—
Gd^{3+}	2.89	110.5	23.0	—
Tb^{3+}	3.56	133.2	12.6	—
Dy^{3+}	5.07	—	8.24	—
Ho^{3+}	8.18	—	—	—
Er^{3+}	16.00	—	1.78	—
Tm^{3+}	—	—	—	—
Yb^{3+}	34.78	—	1.2	—
Lu^{3+}	47.27	—	—	—

* Calculated as anhydrous salt.

most striking with the double sodium, potassium, or thallium(I) sulfates, $Ln_2(SO_4)_3 \cdot M^I_2SO_4 \cdot nH_2O$. However, none of these differences is completely clean-cut, and one group shades into the other.

TABLE 3.8.   General Trends in Solubility in Water

Anion	Cerium group ($Z = 57$–62)	Yttrium group ($Z = 39, 63$–71)
$Cl^-, Br^-, I^-, NO_3^-,$ $ClO_4^-, BrO_3^-,$ $C_2H_3O_2^-$	Soluble	Soluble
F^-	Insoluble	Insoluble
OH^-	Insoluble	Insoluble
HCO_2^-	Slightly soluble	Moderately soluble
$C_2O_4^{2-}$	Insoluble; insoluble in $C_2O_4^{2-}$	Insoluble; soluble in $C_2O_4^{2-}$
CO_3^{2-}	Insoluble; insoluble in CO_3^{2-}	Insoluble; soluble in CO_3^{2-}
Basic NO_3^-	Moderately soluble	Slightly soluble
PO_4^{3-}	Insoluble	Insoluble
Double M^I sulfate	Insoluble in M_2SO_4 solution	Soluble in M_2SO_4 solution

The insolubility of the oxalates, even in dilute acids (pH 4 or less), is both striking and important. Precipitation with oxalic acid under these conditions may be used to separate the tripositive lanthanides from all other cationic species except the tri- and tetrapositive actinides.

Although the oxides and hydroxides are nearly quantitatively insoluble in water, they are sufficiently basic to dissolve readily in acids. Even the ignited oxides dissolve rapidly. Unlike the analogous compounds of common tripositive species (e.g., Al^{3+}, Cr^{3+}, Ga^{3+}), these substances are almost completely unreactive with aqueous alkalies and with basic oxides at elevated temperatures. That the hydrous oxides and hydroxides precipitate at steadily decreasing pH values from the light to the heavy end of the series (e.g., La^{3+}, 7.82; Gd^{3+},

6.83; Lu^{3+}, 6.30—all from nitrate solutions at 25°C.) is an important confirmation of the basicity order.

Complex Species. The importance of these species in the chemistry of the lanthanides may be expected from their importance in that of the *d*-type transition metals. It is observed experimentally, however, that except for the common aquated ions, $[Ln(H_2O)_n]^{3+}$, complex species are limited in number and notably stable only when derived from the strongest chelating agents. Indeed, there is a much greater similarity in behavior to the alkaline earth metal ions than to the *d*-type transition metal ions. This is perhaps not unreasonable when we realize that the transition metal species owe their properties to interaction between the *d* electrons of the valence shell and the ligands. The *f* electrons of the lanthanides are too well shielded to interact similarly, as pointed out in our earlier discussions of magnetic and light absorption properties (pp. 28, 32). The result is that each lanthanide ion is effectively an inert gas-type ion, like those of the alkaline earth metals, that attracts ligands only by over-all electrostatic forces. On this basis, we would expect—and indeed we do observe—a general decrease in case of complex ion formation with a specific ligand in the series $Ln^{4+} > Ln^{3+} > Ln^{2+}$.

Known types of complex species, together with appropriate illustrative examples, are summarized in Table 3.9. Those indicated as ion pair associations exist in solution, where their presence can be inferred from the changes in conductance, transference number, ion migration, or solvent extraction behavior that follow addition of the complexing group. They do not, in general, carry through series of reactions without change, and they are not distinguishable in solid compounds. Of the isolable nonchelated species, only the antipyrene derivatives are stable in contact with water; the others yield hydroxides, indicating that ammonia or the amine is only weakly held.

TABLE 3.9. A Classification of Typical Complex Species Derived from Ln^{3+}

Type	Examples[*]
Ion pair associations	Halo-LnF^{2+}
	Sulfito-$LnSO_3^+$
	Sulfato-$LnSO_4^+$
	Thiosulfato-$LnS_2O_3^+$
	Oxalato-$LnC_2O_4^+$
	Acetato-$LnC_2H_3O_2^{2+}$
Isolable nonchelated species	Ammines: $LnCl_3 \cdot xNH_3$
	Amine adducts: $LnX_3 \cdot yRNH_2$
	Antipyrine adducts:
	$[Ln(ap)_6]X_3$ (X = I, ClO_4, NCS)
Isolable chelated species	
1. Nonionic	8-Quinolinols: $[Ln(On)_3] \cdot nH_2O$
	1,3-Diketones: $[Ln(diket)_3] \cdot H_2O$
2. Ionic	Citrates: $[Ln(C_6H_5O_7)_2]^{3-}$
	α-Hydroxycarboxylates:
	$[Ln(R—CHOHCO_2)_6]^{3-}$
	Aminepolycarboxylates:
	$[Ln(EDTA)]^-$, $[Ln(NTA)_2]^{3-}$

[*] ap =

diket =

On =

For EDTA and NTA see Table 3.10.

The chelated species are much more stable with respect to their components. The nonionic, or *inner complex*, species are difficultly soluble in water but quite soluble in organic solvents such as benzene or chloroform. They are ordinarily obtained by precipitation from aqueous solutions of carefully controlled pH. The 1,3-diketone chelates have the same colors as the aquated tripositive ions, and there are only slight modifications in the absorption bands. The 8-quinolinol chelates are uniformly yellow, as a result of the organic group present, but their absorption spectra consist of sharply defined, weak bands at the wavelengths of those for the aquated ions superimposed on the broad, intense bands of the 8-quinolinol grouping.

The other chelated species mentioned are usually soluble in water, so soluble in fact that crystallization of their salts may be extremely difficult. The formation of such chelated species in aqueous solution involves stepwise equilibria of the type

$$Ln^{3+} + AA \rightleftharpoons Ln(AA) \tag{3-I}$$

$$Ln(AA) + AA \rightleftharpoons Ln(AA)_2 \tag{3-II}$$

$$Ln(AA)_2 + (n - 2)AA \rightleftharpoons Ln(AA)_n \tag{3-III}$$

or, for the final substance, the over-all equilibrium

$$Ln^{3+} + nAA \rightleftharpoons Ln(AA)_n \tag{3-IV}$$

where AA is the chelating group and both aquation and the charges of the chelated species are neglected. The displacement of each such equilibrium, and therefore the stability of the species in question with respect to its components, is measured quantitatively by the magnitude of the appropriate equilibrium constant. Thus for equilibrium 3-IV this would be

$$K_{Ln(AA)_n} = c_{Ln(AA)_n}/c_{Ln^{3+}}c_{AA}^n \tag{3.1}$$

Constants of this type are called *formation* or *stability constants*. For convenience, $\log_{10} K$ values (see Table 3.11), rather than the formation constants themselves, are usually used.

Undeniably, the most stable, and at the same time the most interesting and useful, chelated species of the lanthanides are those derived from the aminepolycarboxylic acids. As is indicated by the graphic formulas given in Table 3.10, the

TABLE 3.10. Aminepolycarboxylic Acids

Name	Formula	Possible chelate rings
Nitrilotriacetic acid (H₃NTA)	$N{<}^{CH_2COOH}_{\ CH_2COOH}$ with CH_2COOH	3
N-Hydroxyethylethylenediamine-triacetic acid (H₃HEDTA)	$HOCH_2CH_2{\diagdown}NCH_2CH_2N{<}^{CH_2COOH}_{\ CH_2COOH}$, $HOOCCH_2{\diagup}$	4
Ethylenediaminetetraacetic acid (H₄EDTA)	$HOOCCH_2{\diagdown}NCH_2CH_2N{<}^{CH_2COOH}_{\ CH_2COOH}$, $HOOCCH_2{\diagup}$	5
1,2-Diaminocyclohexanetetraacetic acid (H₄DCTA)	$CH_2{-}CH_2{\diagdown}CHN{<}^{CH_2COOH}_{\ CH_2COOH}$, $CH_2{-}CH_2{\diagup}CHN{<}^{CH_2COOH}_{\ CH_2COOH}$	5
Diethylenetriaminepentaacetic acid (H₅DTPA)	$HOOCCH_2{\diagdown}NCH_2CH_2NCH_2CH_2N{<}^{CH_2COOH}_{\ CH_2COOH}$, $HOOCCH_2{\diagup}$ with $CH_2{-}COOH$	7

anions of these acids are each capable of forming more than one chelate ring by utilizing the several oxygen and nitrogen donors that are available. Indeed, in every instance there are sufficient donors present that 1:1 species result (e.g., $Ln(EDTA)^-$, $Ln(DTPA)^{2-}$). Formation constant data for a number of these systems are summarized in Table 3.11 and Fig. 3.1.

It is apparent that an increase in the number of like chelate rings in which a given cation can simultaneously participate increases the formation constant or stability. This is a general observation and principle. For a given ligand, the general increase in stability with decrease in crystal radius that we have predicted is observed. However, a closer examination of these and other data shows that although this increase is invariable

TABLE 3.11. Stabilities of Some Aminepolycarboxylic Acid Chelates at 25°C.

	$\log_{10} K_{Ln(AA)}$				
Cation	AA = NTA	AA = HEDTA	AA = EDTA[*]	AA = DCTA	AA = DTPA
Y^{3+}	11.48	14.65	18.09	19.41	22.05
La^{3+}	10.36	13.46	15.50	16.35	19.48
Ce^{3+}	10.83	14.11	15.98	—	20.5
Pr^{3+}	11.07	14.61	16.40	17.23	21.07
Nd^{3+}	11.26	14.86	16.61	17.69	21.60
Pm^{3+}	—	—	—	—	—
Sm^{3+}	11.53	15.28	17.14	18.63	22.34
Eu^{3+}	11.52	15.35	17.35	18.77	22.39
Gd^{3+}	11.54	15.22	17.37	18.80	22.46
Tb^{3+}	11.59	15.32	17.93	19.30	22.71
Dy^{3+}	11.74	15.30	18.30	19.69	22.82
Ho^{3+}	11.90	15.32	—	19.89	22.78
Er^{3+}	12.03	15.42	18.85	20.20	22.74
Tm^{3+}	12.22	15.59	19.32	20.46	22.72
Yb^{3+}	12.40	15.88	19.51	20.80	22.62
Lu^{3+}	12.49	15.88	19.83	20.91	22.44
Al^{3+}	—	—	16.13	17.63[*]	—
Fe^{3+}	15.87[*]	—	25.1	—	28.6
Co^{3+}	—	—	36	—	—

[*] At 20°C.

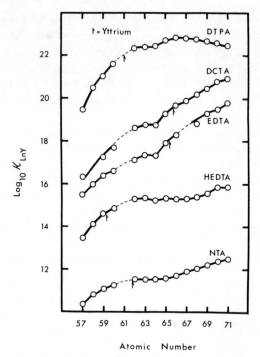

Fig. 3.1. Stabilities of Ln^{III}-aminepolycarboxylate chelates.

in the region La^{3+} through Eu^{3+}, with something of a break or discontinuity at the Gd^{3+} ion, two different behaviors characterize the region Gd^{3+} through Lu^{3+}, namely:

1. A continuing and rather regular increase in stability, with the yttrium chelate occupying the position expected from the crystal radius of the Y^{3+} ion (e.g., with NTA, EDTA, DCTA).

2. An increase in stability, followed by a decrease or a leveling off to essential constancy, with the yttrium chelate occupying a position in the Nd^{3+}–Sm^{3+} region and completely

out of line with that expected on a size basis (e.g., with HEDTA, DTPA).

Thus the concept of an electrostatic attraction between cation and ligand that increases as crystal radius decreases appears reasonable for the lighter lanthanides, but it is apparent that additional factors are also of importance among the heavier lanthanides. What these factors are and how they operate are not presently understood. It is probable that they reflect the fact that the formation constant really measures the displacement of an equilibrium of the type

$$[Ln(H_2O)_n]^{3+} + EDTA^{4-} \rightleftharpoons [Ln(EDTA)(H_2O)_m]^- +$$
$$(n - m)\,H_2O$$

where EDTA is cited as typical, rather than the reaction of the anhydrous cation. The smoothing effect of hydration on crystal radii, the rupture of $Ln{-}OH_2$ bonds, the formation of new bonds, and the retention of water in the product are undoubtedly important in determining the measured stability.

It is tempting to associate the *gadolinium break* (Fig. 3.1) with the corresponding break in crystal radii (Fig. 2.1), but the latter is insufficient alone to account for the former. Furthermore, the nomadic behavior of yttrium is not limited to chelated species. Thus, in fractional precipitation, yttrium may concentrate with either the lighter (using $Fe(CN)_6^{3-}$ or $Fe(CN)_6^{4-}$) or the heavier (using OH^-) lanthanides. Clearly, we have here both an indication that our simple approach to basicity is not completely adequate and a warning that what is observed for the lighter cations cannot always be extrapolated to the heavier. The fundamental value of experimental observation cannot be overemphasized (p. 33).

Differences in formation constant between adjacent cations are somewhat larger for the aminepolycarboxylates than for other known ligands, except possibly some of the α-hydroxycarboxylates. These differences are used to advantage in both laboratory and practical separations (pp. 80–88). As indicated by the comparison data in Table 3.11, the formation constants associated with similar chelates of more familiar tripositive ions are larger. This probably reflects the greater importance of covalent bonding.

The compositions of some of the species mentioned suggest a *coordination number* of *six* for each of the Ln^{3+} ions. This coordination number has been assumed for many years. However, facts such as the invariable presence of bound water in 1,3-diketone and aminepolycarboxylate complex species and the ability of [Ln(NTA)] compounds to form readily $[Ln(NTA)_2]^{3-}$ ions suggest a larger coordination number than six, at least *seven* but perhaps even *eight* or *nine*. Thus far, we do not know with certainty.

Unlike the *d*-type transition metal ions, the lanthanides do not form π-type complex species with unsaturated hydrocarbons (e.g., olefins, cyclopentadiene).[*] Indeed, a complete study of the cyclopentadienides, $Ln(C_5H_5)_3$ (Table 2.6), indicates that these compounds are salts rather than complex compounds.

Oxidation State + 4—Another "Anomalous" State

Inasmuch as cerium(IV) oxide is formed when an alkaline suspension of cerium(III) hydroxide is exposed to the atmosphere or treated with chlorine or hydrogen peroxide or when many cerium(III) salts containing oxy anions are heated in the air, it is probable that tetrapositive cerium was recognized even in early studies of the lanthanides. Indeed, under the conditions outlined, the tetrapositive state is so readily formed at the expense of the tripositive that it has often been regarded

---

[*] Doubly occupied *p*-type atomic orbitals of carbon atoms in such hydrocarbons may interact by a sidewise overlap with vacant orbitals of cations to give so-called π bonds.

as the more completely characteristic oxidation state. The other tetrapositive lanthanides, however, are encountered only in solid compounds (Table 2.2) that undergo reduction when dissolved.

Chemical Stability and Stabilization. It is thus convenient to discuss cerium separately. The listed standard oxidation potential (Table 2.3) describes the equilibrium

$$Ce(aq)^{3+} \rightleftharpoons Ce(aq)^{4+} + e$$

when neither complexing by the anion nor hydrolysis occurs. However, experimentally measured potentials vary widely as these reactions become important (e.g., for solutions $1N$ in the acid indicated: $HClO_4$, -1.70 v.; HNO_3, -1.61 v.; H_2SO_4, -1.44 v.). Correction for these effects gives the listed value.

In acidic media, cerium(IV) is slightly stronger as an oxidizing agent than lead(IV) oxide and slightly weaker than hydrogen peroxide. It can be formed from cerium(III) by only a few chemical oxidizing agents (e.g., $S_2O_8^{2-}$, O_3) and is best prepared by electrolytic oxidation. On the other hand, reduction is readily effected by many reagents (e.g., Fe^{2+}, Sn^{2+}, I^-, H_2O_2, organic compounds). That the change is a completely reversible, one-electron change makes cerium(IV) a particularly useful analytical oxidant. Although no potential data are available for alkaline systems, experiment shows that there cerium(IV) is a much weaker oxidizing agent.

Hydrated cerium(IV) oxide dissolves without reduction in nitric, perchloric, or sulfuric acid. Such solutions readily hydrolyze and deposit basic salts as the acidity is reduced, but if the acidity is kept sufficiently high they can yield hydrated cerium(IV) salts. In the presence of ammonium nitrate, the orange-red double salt $Ce(NO_3)_4 \cdot 2NH_4NO_3$ is easily crystallized. This is a common water-soluble source of cerium(IV).   A comparable double sulfate, $Ce(SO_4)_2 \cdot 2(NH_4)_2SO_4 \cdot 2H_2O$, can be prepared also. In the solid state, cerium(IV) is substantially stabilized as the oxide (CeO_2) or fluoride (CeF_4).

The other tetrapositive species (Pr^{IV}, Nd^{IV}, Tb^{IV}, Dy^{IV}) apparently require trapping in a suitable crystal lattice for their stabilization. The estimated potential of -2.86 v. for the Pr^{III}–Pr^{IV} couple suggests that praseodymium(IV) is comparable to elemental fluorine in oxidizing strength in acidic solution. It is probable that the other tetrapositive species are at least as strongly oxidizing.

Stabilization in the Solid State. Except for cerium(IV), where any preparable solid resists reduction, only oxide and fluoride systems are known to stabilize tetrapositive species.

1. *Oxide Systems.*   The common compounds are off-white to brownish CeO_2, black Pr_6O_{11}, and dark brown Tb_4O_7, although both PrO_2 and TbO_2 have been prepared. The formulations Pr_6O_{11} and Tb_4O_7 represent average analytical compositions, rather than true compounds, but they suggest that compounds intermediate in analysis between $LnO_{1.5}$ (i.e., Ln_2O_3) and LnO_2 can be obtained. This is experimentally true. As is shown by Fig. 3.2, there is a continuous decrease in the lattice dimension a as one increases the mole ratio of oxygen to lanthanide in both the praseodymium–oxygen and the terbium–oxygen systems. This includes those of the oxides Pr_6O_{11} and Tb_4O_7. Since this suggests continuous alteration in composition without substantial change in crystal structure, we must ask how this can be possible.

The three distinguishable forms of the sesquioxides (Ln_2O_3) have the broad regions of existence noted in Fig. 3.3. The A type (hexagonal, with seven oxide ions surrounding each Ln^{3+} ion) and the B type (monoclinic, with some Ln^{3+} ions surrounded by six oxide ions and others by seven) are less important in this connection than the C type (cubic), the

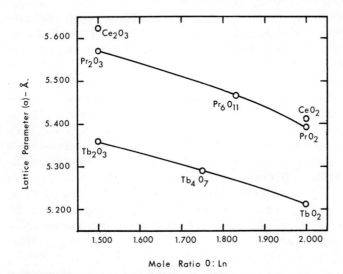

Fig. 3.2. Variation in lattice parameter with O:Ln ratio. (Redrawn from Gruen, D. M., Koehler, W. C., and Katz, J. J., *J. Am. Chem. Soc.* **73,** 1475 (1951).)

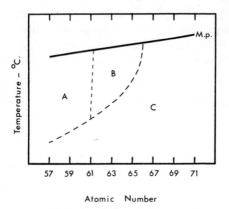

Fig. 3.3. Regions of existence of crystal modifications of Ln_2O_3 (not drawn to scale).

structure of which is shown in comparison with the cubic fluorite-type structure of the oxides LnO_2 in Fig. 3.4. In the fluorite arrangement, each Ln^{4+} ion is surrounded by eight oxide ions at the corners of a regular cube. The C-type Ln_2O_3 arrangement differs only in the fact that one-fourth of these oxygen positions are not used. Thus, by adding oxygen one can transfer from the $LnO_{1.50}$ composition to the LnO_2 without altering the fundamental nature of the structure. As a consequence, any number of intermediate compositions might be distinguished, e.g., $PrO_{1.71}$, $PrO_{1.77}$, $PrO_{1.66}$, $TbO_{1.71}$, $TbO_{1.81}$. Correspondingly, two different lanthanides can appear in the same oxide crystal if the lattice dimensions (a) of $LnO_{2.00}$ and C-$LnO_{1.50}$ are not markedly different ($\pm 2.25\%$). For example, the oxides CeO_2 and Ln_2O_3 form homogeneous crystals for Ln = Y and Pm–Lu. The lattice dimensions (a) of the LnO_2 oxides are CeO_2, 5.411 Å.; PrO_2, 5.395 Å.; TbO_2, 5.213 Å. Again the lanthanide contraction is apparent.

These relationships provide an explanation for the observations that oxidation of cerium(III) hydroxide or oxide gives products that are green, blue, and purple before the final off-white to pale yellow CeO_2 is obtained and that cerium(IV) oxide darkens when heated. These products owe their color to the presence of both tri- and tetravalent cerium in the same crystal. Mixed-valence compounds of a given element are

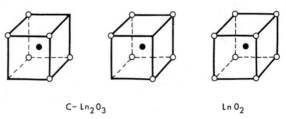

$$C-Ln_2O_3 \qquad\qquad Ln\,O_2$$

Fig. 3.4. Comparison of crystal structures of C-type Ln_2O_3 and LnO_2 ($\circ$ = O^{2-}; $\bullet$ = Ln^{3+} or Ln^{4+}).

often deeply colored, even though color is absent when but a single oxidation state is present.

2. *Fluoride Systems.* Although the compound CeF_4 was prepared many years ago, the terbium analog was not obtained until 1954. It is colorless and isostructural with the cerium(IV) compound. Pure praseodymium(IV) fluoride has not been prepared. However, the complex compounds $Na[PrF_5]$ and $M_2[PrF_6]$ (M = Na, K, Rb, Cs) have been obtained and have been shown to contain praseodymium(IV) by analysis, magnetic measurements, absorption spectra, and X-ray evaluation of structure. Analogous terbium compounds $M_2[TbF_6]$ (M = K, Rb, Cs) have been prepared. Both neodymium and dysprosium yield the apparently isomorphous compounds $Cs_3[LnF_7]$ (Ln = Nd, Dy).

Preparation. General methods of obtaining the tetrapositive species include

1. *Oxidation with oxygen at elevated temperatures.* Ignition in air of salts containing thermally decomposable oxy anions (e.g., OH^-, CO_3^{2-}, $C_2O_4^{2-}$) or of the sesquioxides gives the oxides CeO_2, Pr_6O_{11}, and Tb_4O_7. The stoichiometric oxide PrO_2 results when the sesquioxide is heated in oxygen at 100 atmospheres of pressure at 500°C. Heating the sesquioxide with atomic oxygen at 450°C. gives the oxide TbO_2.

2. *Oxidation with fluorine at elevated temperatures.* Elemental fluorine at 300–500°C. converts the trifluorides to CeF_4 and TbF_4. Treating mixtures of alkali metal chlorides and the trichlorides of praseodymium, neodymium, and dysprosium with elemental fluorine at 300–500°C. yields the solids $Na[PrF_5]$, $M_2[PrF_6]$, $Cs_3[NdF_7]$, and $Cs_3[DyF_7]$.

3. *Chemical oxidation at ordinary temperatures.* Cerium(III) oxide or the hydrous hydroxide slowly absorbs atmospheric oxygen and ultimately yields the dioxide. This oxidation is more rapid with alkaline hydrogen peroxide or sodium hypochlorite. Both bromate ion and permanganate ion oxidize

cerium(III) ion to the dioxide in suitably buffered solutions. Peroxydisulfate yields cerium(IV) ion under acidic conditions.

In Conclusion

The general chemistry of the lanthanides, as just presented, both implements the conceptual approach followed in Chapter 2 and provides the background essential to understanding the problems of recovery, separation, and application to be discussed in Chapter 4. We see that in the main experimental observation is in accord with the broad theoretical background that has been developed but that there are instances of difference where modification of this background is essential. We shall see that a combination of this background with the factual information given has done much to reduce the complex problems of separation to logical routine.

Selected Readings

Asprey, L. B., and Cunningham, B. B., "Progress in Inorganic Chemistry," F. A. Cotton, Ed., Vol. II, pp. 267–86, Interscience Publishers, New York, 1960. (Anomalous oxidation states.)

Daane, A. H., "The Rare Earths," F. H. Spedding and A. H. Daane, Eds., ch. 13, John Wiley & Sons, New York, 1961. (Metals.)

Daane, A. H., "Rare Metals Handbook," C. A. Hampel, Ed., ch. 33, Reinhold Publishing Corp., New York, 1961. (Yttrium metal.)

Kremers, H. E., "Rare Metals Handbook," C. A. Hampel, Ed., ch. 19, Reinhold Publishing Corp., New York, 1961. (Metals.)

Pearce, D. W., *Chem. Rev.* **16,** 121–47 (1935). (Anomalous oxidation states.)

Pearce, D. W., and Selwood, P. W., *J. Chem. Educ.* **13,** 224–230 (1936). (Anomalous oxidation states.)

Vickery, R. C., "Chemistry of the Lanthanons," ch. 8, 13, 14, Academic Press, New York, 1953. (General chemistry.)

Yost, D. M., Russell, H., Jr., and Garner, C. S., "The Rare-Earth Elements and Their Compounds," ch. 6, John Wiley & Sons, New York, 1947. (General chemistry.)

chapter four

OCCURRENCE, RECOVERY, SEPARATION, APPLICATION— THE REALM OF THE PRACTICAL

Thus far, we have obviously—and indeed very deliberately—assigned the practical aspects of the chemistry of the lanthanides to a subordinate role. The wisdom of this somewhat unconventional procedure lies in the extreme difficulty of considering the practical in any ordered or logical fashion without some prior knowledge of why these substances behave as they do, of what similarities and differences among them can be exploited, and of what commonplace and unusual properties they have. This background permits us to systematize our discussion and to make the practical a unified part of the whole.

Occurrence in Nature

The abundance data already cited (Table 1.3) indicate only that as a group and, in certain instances as individuals, the lanthanides are potentially available in unlimited quantities. A complete picture of availability, however, must include also data on concentrations of these species in economically interesting deposits. Here, the nature of the minerals available, the ease with which such minerals can be cracked and thus the cost of processing, the geographical location of ore bodies, and the markets for products are all of importance.

As may be expected from similarities in crystal radii, oxidation state, and general properties (Chapters 2 and 3), each known lanthanide mineral contains all members of the series (except, presumably, promethium). This is true of even cerite or gadolinite, although the historical developments outlined in Chapter 1 might suggest otherwise. It is observed, of course, that natural processes of geochemical concentration have given us certain minerals rich in the cerium group (p. 51) and others rich in the yttrium group. This tendency for cations of closely similar radii to concentrate in particular minerals accounts also for the natural occurrence of yttrium in association with the heavier lanthanides.

Important cerium and yttrium group minerals, together with their compositions and the geographical locations of their most important deposits, are summarized in Table 4.1.

Monazite, both because of its availability and substantial thorium content, is the most important of the mineral sources. Although massive monazite crystals are found in many pegmatites, in only a few instances (notably in South Africa) are they present in sufficient quantity to permit vein mining. Natural weathering and gravity concentration processes (sp. gr. of monazite = 5.2), however, have produced sizable placer deposits of monazite sands. The most notable of these are in Travancore, where the beach deposits are seemingly limitless and regenerate with each crest of tide. Commercial mining of monazite sands in the United States has centered in Florida and the Carolinas, the substantial Idaho deposits being diffi-

TABLE 4.1. Important Minerals

	Composition[*]		Location of significant deposits
Name	Idealized	Generalized	
1. Cerium Group Minerals			
Monazite	$(Ce)PO_4$	49–74% Ce earths 1–4% Y earths 5–9% ThO_2 1–2% SiO_2 tr. U	Travancore, India; Brazil; Union of South Africa; Florida, North and South Carolina, Idaho
Bastnaesite	$(Ce)FCO_3$	65–70% Ce earths < 1% Y earths	California, New Mexico; Sweden
Cerite	$(Ce)_3M^{II}H_3Si_3O_{13}$ (M = Ca, Fe)	51–72% Ce earths tr.–7.6% Y earths tr. Th, U, Zr	Sweden; Caucausus
2. Yttrium Group Minerals			
Euxenite[†]	$(Y)(Nb,Ta)TiO_6 \cdot$ xH_2O	13–35% Y earths 2–8% Ce earths 20–23% TiO_2 25–35% $(Nb,Ta)_2O_5$	Australia; Idaho
Xenotime	$(Y)PO_4$	54–65% Y earths ca. 0.1% Ce earths up to 3% ThO_2 up to 3.5% U_3O_8 2–3% ZrO_2	Norway; Brazil
Gadolinite	$(Y)_2M^{II}_3Si_2O_{10}$ (M = Fe, Be)	35–48% Y earths 2–17% Ce earths up to 11.6% BeO tr. Th	Sweden; Norway; Texas, Colorado

[*] The symbols (Ce) and (Y) represent the cerium and yttrium group lanthanides, respectively.

[†] Name used when $(Nb,Ta)_2O_5/TiO_2 = 1:4$ or more; when this ratio is 1:3 or less, the mineral is polycrase.

cultly accessible.   Other heavy minerals such as zircon, ilmenite, garnet, and rutile are common contaminants in monazite deposits. The large bastnaesite deposits at Mountain Pass, California, represent a potentially competitive mineral source of negligible thorium content. Cerite is only of historical interest.

The yttrium group lanthanides are recovered commercially from monazite concentrates, even though their over-all concentration is low. Both gadolinite and euxenite are sufficiently abundant to be of potential commercial interest. Commercial processing of the latter (e.g., from Idaho) for niobium and tantalum gives the mixed lanthanides as by-products. Xenotime is found in small quantities in monazite sands.

Gross Recovery from Mineral Sources

Similarities between laboratory and technical approaches make it impractical, either here or later, to distinguish between them.   Processing amounts to cracking the mineral, recovering the lanthanides (and thorium), removing thorium if it is present, and separating the lanthanides. It is ordinarily most convenient to remove cerium before fractionating the other lanthanides.

Cracking and Recovery Procedures.   The chemical treatment used depends upon the composition of the mineral.   The silicate minerals are conveniently decomposed to insoluble silica and the soluble chlorides by digestion with hydrochloric acid.   Euxenite may be treated with hydrofluoric acid to solubilize the niobium, tantalum, and titanium values and leave the insoluble lanthanide fluorides.   Monazite (or xenotime) is decomposed by digestion with either concentrated sulfuric acid or sodium hydroxide solution.   Bastnaesite is converted by concentrated sulfuric acid to the water-soluble sulfates, with the loss of gaseous carbon dioxide and hydrogen fluoride.

The sulfuric acid treatment of monazite sand may be summarized as shown in Scheme 4.1. From the resulting solution, thorium can be precipitated as a phosphate by diluting to the proper acidity or as the fluoride by adding hydrofluoric acid and taking advantage of the greater solubility of the LnF_3 compounds in strongly acidic solutions. In either procedure, the lanthanides must be separated from phosphate species by precipitation as hydrous hydroxides or oxalates. Alternatively, both the thorium and the lanthanides can be freed of phosphate by precipitation as oxalates and conversion to the more reactive hydrous oxides or hydroxides with caustic soda.

The sodium hydroxide treatment of monazite sand may be summarized as in Scheme 4.2. This procedure has the advantage of removing phosphate more readily than the sulfuric acid procedure, but its higher cost has limited its adoption.

Removal of Thorium. In addition to the procedures mentioned, the following have been used:

1. *Selective precipitation* as ThO_2 (with sodium hydroxide at pH 5.8, or with reagents such as $S_2O_3^{2-}$ or $(CH_2)_6N_4$ that control pH appropriately by hydrolysis); as $Th(IO_3)_4$ from concentrated HNO_3 solution); or as ThP_2O_6 (from strongly acidic solution). None of these procedures is completely specific, since each depends only on the lower solubility of the thorium compound under optimum conditions.

2. *Selective extraction into nonaqueous solvents*, such as tri-*n*-butyl phosphate or certain higher amines, whereby thorium is more readily transferred to the nonaqueous phase than the lanthanides. Tri-*n*-butyl phosphate systems are discussed later (pp. 88, 90) with specific reference to the lanthanides. The amines function best with sulfate solution, from which thorium is removed as the amine salt of a sulfato complex (e.g., (amine $\cdot$ H)$_2$[Th(SO$_4$)$_3$]) completely and in a high state of purity.

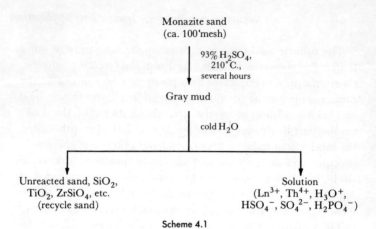

Monazite sand
(ca. 100'mesh)

$93\%\ H_2SO_4$,
$210°C.$,
several hours

Gray mud

cold H_2O

Unreacted sand, SiO_2,
TiO_2, $ZrSiO_4$, etc.
(recycle sand)

Solution
(Ln^{3+}, Th^{4+}, H_3O^+,
HSO_4^-, SO_4^{2-}, $H_2PO_4^-$)

Scheme 4.1

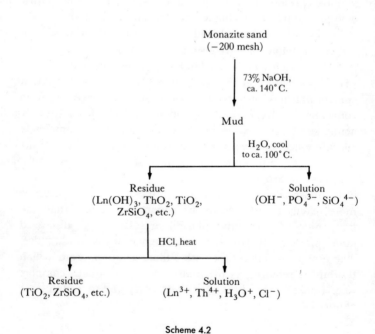

Monazite sand
(-200 mesh)

$73\%\ NaOH$,
ca. $140°C.$

Mud

H_2O, cool
to ca. $100°C.$

Residue
($Ln(OH)_3$, ThO_2, TiO_2,
$ZrSiO_4$, etc.)

Solution
(OH^-, PO_4^{3-}, SiO_4^{4-})

HCl, heat

Residue
(TiO_2, $ZrSiO_4$, etc.)

Solution
(Ln^{3+}, Th^{4+}, H_3O^+, Cl^-)

Scheme 4.2

72

3. *Selective anion exchange*, whereby an amine-type exchanger removes thorium as a nitrato or sulfato complex ion. The separation is rapid and complete.

Removal of Cerium. Useful procedures are based upon reduced basicity in the tetrapositive state. They include:

1. *Selective reaction of the mixed oxides with nitric acid (pH 3–4)*, in which the reduced solubility of cerium(IV) results in its concentration in the residues, but not in its complete separation.

2. *Selective hydrolysis* to a basic nitrate or sulfate as a result of diluting and boiling a concentrated solution containing Ce^{4+} and Ln^{3+} ions. Although some three-fourths of the cerium is obtained in a high state of purity, complete separation cannot be achieved.

3. *Selective oxidation*, anodically or chemically with bromate or permanganate, followed by *nearly* complete precipitation of cerium(IV) from the buffered solution.

4. *Selective crystallization* of the double ammonium nitrate (p. 61) from nitric acid solutions. Separation from the tripositive species is complete, but recovery is not quantitative.

5. *Selective extraction into nonaqueous solvents*, especially tri-*n*-butyl phosphate, where cerium(IV) parallels thorium in behavior. Reduction with aqueous sodium nitrite returns cerium (as Ce^{3+}) to the aqueous phase, but leaves thorium in the nonaqueous.

Separation of the Lanthanides

Separation may be effected by one or another or some combination of the following general procedures involving

1. Fractional crystallization of isomorphous salts
2. Basicity differences
   a. Fractional precipitation from solution
   b. Fractional thermal decomposition of salts
   c. Ion exchange

    d. Solvent extraction
3. Selective oxidation or reduction
4. Physical differences

All procedures, except certain of those involving oxidation or reduction, are fractional in character. Thus in each step there is a concentration of one species at the expense of the other, but separation results only if that step is repeated many times.

The efficiency of a fractionation procedure is given by the magnitude of its *separation factor*. For two lanthanides, Ln and Ln', being changed from an initial concentration condition (1) to a final one (2), the separation factor (α) may be defined as

$$\alpha = \frac{c_{Ln(2)} / c_{Ln'(2)}}{c_{Ln(1)} / c_{Ln'(1)}} = \frac{c_{Ln(2)} c_{Ln'(1)}}{c_{Ln(1)} c_{Ln'(2)}} \tag{4.1}$$

No separation results if $\alpha = 1$, but the greater the departure from unity, the more efficient the process is.

Methods of Following Separations. It is important that the path taken by each component be followed analytically as fractionation proceeds, preferably by a rapid procedure that is specific for each cation and does not destroy or alter the sample. Spectrophotometric procedures are the most generally useful. Each absorbing tripositive species has bands (Table 2.9) free from interference by other cations that adhere to the Beer-Lambert relationship

$$\log_{10} I_0/I = kcl \tag{4.2}$$

where I_0 and I are the intensities of the incident and transmitted light, c is concentration, l is the light path, and k is a constant. Secondary X-ray fluorescence is also useful, but emission spectrographic procedures are best applied only to the detection and determination of small quantities of contaminants in highly purified samples.

Magnetic susceptibility data (pp. 26, 28) are of analytical significance only for binary mixtures of paramagnetic substances of known moments or of a paramagnetic and a diamagnetic substance. Average atomic weight, based usually upon the results of analyses of the mixed oxalates for both lanthanide and oxalate content, although of historical importance, is of quantitative significance only for a binary mixture or a sample containing yttrium. The lower atomic weight of yttrium (88.905) compared with those of the lanthanides (138.91–174.97) permits one to follow it by this means.

Inasmuch as little of the early work on separations could be followed quantitatively, it is impossible to judge the efficiencies of many of the procedures described.

Fractional Crystallization. The quantity of work reported and the amount of information accumulated relating to this classical procedure (Chapter 1) are truly overwhelming. It is probable that every anion found to form soluble salts with the tripositive ions has been investigated in the hope of developing an efficient crystallization separation. Inasmuch as only those anions yielding truly isomorphous salts that are easy to crystallize, have reasonable and temperature-dependent solubilities, and possess measurable solubility differences as the Ln^{3+} ion changes can be effective, the number of really successful systems must be limited.

Both fractional crystallization and fractional precipitation involve the formation of a solid phase from a solution phase and can thus be described similarly in terms of separation factor. Separation factors for several procedures of this type, as calculated from Eq. 4.1, are summarized in Table 4.2. These can be criticized on the ground that the slow equilibration necessary to produce the completely homogeneous solid phase required by Eq. 4.1 is seldom realized in practice. Rather, the true equilibrium is normally between the solution and an infinitesimally thin layer at the crystal surface. Under

TABLE 4.2. Separation Factors for Fractional Crystallization and Precipitation Processes[*]

Procedure	Ion pair	α
Double ammonium nitrate crystallization	$La^{3+}-Nd^{3+}$	3.1
Dimethyl oxalate precipitation	$La^{3+}-Pr^{3+}$	4.9
Alkali carbonate precipitation	$La^{3+}-Nd^{3+}$	4.9
Magnesium oxide precipitation	$La^{3+}-Nd^{3+}$	5.6

[*] Data from Weaver, B., *Anal. Chem.* **26,** 474 (1954).

these conditions, the separation factor is given more exactly by the logarithmic expression

$$\alpha' = \log_{10}(c_{Ln(2)}/c_{Ln(1)})/\log_{10}(c_{Ln'(2)}/c_{Ln'(1)}) \qquad (4.3)$$

The data in Table 4.3 suggest that for a given separation α' is more nearly constant than α. Although qualitatively either α or α' could be used to compare the efficiencies of two procedures, very few of the data available on fractional crystallization can be used to evaluate either factor.

TABLE 4.3. Comparison of Homogeneous (α) and Logarithmic (α') Separation Factors for Precipitation by Hydrolysis ot Methyl Oxalate[*]

Cerium(III) precipitated, %	Neodymium(III) coprecipitated, %	α	α'
15.0	24.6	1.85	1.74
21.1	35.4	1.93	1.74
34.2	53.9	2.25	1.85
56.0	76.7	2.53	1.75
62.7	82.7	2.85	1.78
74.4	90.2	3.17	1.71
83.9	95.9	4.49	1.75
92.0	99.0	8.26	1.80

[*] Feibush, A. M., Rowley, K., and Gordon, L., *Anal. Chem.* **30,** 1605 (1958). See also Salutsky, M. L., and Gordon, L., *Anal. Chem.* **28,** 138 (1956).

Among the more effective compounds are

1. The double ammonium nitrates, $Ln(NO_3)_3 \cdot 2NH_4NO_3 \cdot 4H_2O$, for the removal of lanthanum and the separation of praseodymium from neodymium (pp. 4, 78).

2. The double manganese nitrates, $2Ln(NO_3)_3 \cdot 3Mn(NO_3)_2 \cdot 24H_2O$, for the separation of members of the cerium group but not the yttrium group.

3. The bromates, $Ln(BrO_3)_3 \cdot 9H_2O$, and the ethyl sulfates, $Ln(C_2H_5SO_4)_3 \cdot 9H_2O$, for the separation of members of the yttrium group.

Crystallization in each instance is from water. The procedure followed with the double ammonium nitrates is typical. The appropriate solution containing the mixed cations is evaporated until about half of the salts present will crystallize upon cooling to room temperature. The crystals are separated from the mother liquor. Each fraction is then recrystallized, the initial crystals by dissolving in water and evaporating until half the material deposits and the mother liquor by evaporating directly. Four fractions result. The mother liquor from the first crystals in this step is then combined with the second crystals, and the operation repeated. In this way, the triangular scheme shown in Fig. 4.1 is developed, with the least soluble double ammonium nitrate (that of La^{3+}) concentrating at the *head* (crystal end) of the series, the moderately soluble ones (Pr^{3+}, Nd^{3+}) at the center, and the most soluble one (Sm^{3+}) at the *tail* (solution end).

It is apparent that a triangular scheme of this type can expand into a large number of fractions of steadily decreasing content of lanthanides unless some means of control is used. In practice, it is found desirable to omit certain portions of the scheme, thus permitting removal of one lanthanide in a state of purity and treatment of remaining mixed species as a single species. It is found that if the same weight fraction of a

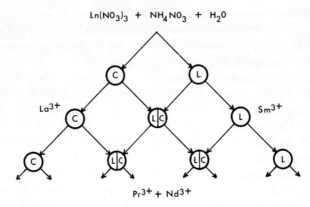

Fig. 4.1. Triangular fractional crystallization scheme for cerium earth double ammonium nitrates.

given component is allowed to crystallize in each step, fractions of repeating total composition result. These may be removed and combined, and more of the original mixture may be added when a fraction that repeats its composition is obtained.

Fractional crystallization is normally most effective at the lanthanum end of the series where solubilities differ the most. Pure lanthanum is quite readily separated as the double ammonium nitrate, but no other fractional crystallization procedure is now of commercial importance. Generally, separations in the samarium-europium-gadolinium region and within the yttrium group are particularly tedious and inefficient; pioneering studies often involved hundreds or even thousands of crystallizations.

If bismuth(III) nitrate is added to a mixture of cerium group nitrates containing magnesium ion, its double magnesium nitrate crystallizes between the isomorphous ones of samarium and europium. From the resulting Sm^{3+}–Bi^{3+} and

$Bi^{3+}-Eu^{3+}$ mixtures, bismuth can be removed readily with hydrogen sulfide. Bismuth(III) is apparently unique among the nonlanthanides as a separating ion, but easily removable lanthanides (e.g., Ce^{3+} between La^{3+} and Pr^{3+} in the double ammonium nitrates or Pr^{3+} between Er^{3+} and Tm^{3+} in the bromates) may function similarly.

Fractional Precipitation. This is somewhat more limited in practicality than fractional crystallization because of the added tedium of removing and redissolving precipitates. Although fractional precipitation reflects the basicity order more nearly exactly than fractional crystallization, yttrium is much more migratory in behavior during precipitation than during crystallization (p. 59).

All separations by fractional precipitation depend fundamentally upon basicity differences. However, these differences can be operative only when equilibration between solution and solid phases is complete. This condition seldom pertains in practice, for addition of a precipitating anion to the mixed lanthanides results in a localized excess of reagent and precipitation of all the species present. Redissolution may then be too slow or too far from complete to permit true equilibration before more reagent is added.

For the specific case of a gaseous reagent such as ammonia, this problem is avoided by introducing the gas extensively diluted with unreactive nitrogen. More generally, it is solved by generating the precipitating ion slowly and homogeneously throughout the solution. Cases in point include hydroxyl ion generated by the cathodic decomposition of water; carbonate and hydroxyl ions formed by adding urea and heating; carbonate ion produced by thermally hydrolyzing trichloroacetate ion; and oxalate ion produced by thermally hydrolyzing dimethyl oxalate. Precipitates so formed are commonly granular and easy to handle. Control of the precipitating reagent by addition of another species that may give a complex species has the same effect. This is exemplified by the use of zinc or cadmium ion with ammonia. Similarly, addition of solid oxides (e.g., MgO, Ln_2O_3) or carbonates (e.g., $PbCO_3$, $ZnCO_3$) provides a slowly increasing and controlled source of hydroxyl ion.

True basicity effects are also achieved by adding a weak complexing agent or insufficient complexing agent (e.g., $EDTA^{4-}$ or NTA^{3-}) to tie up all of the lanthanide ions before adding the precipitant. In either case, the least readily complexed cation is the most available for precipitation.

Although fractional precipitation was once of particular importance in separating yttrium from the heavier lanthanons, it is now of little practical importance.

Fractional Thermal Decomposition of Salts. The temperature at which an oxy salt (e.g., nitrate, sulfate, acetate) is converted to an oxide or basic salt of lower solubility decreases with decreasing basicity of the tripositive cation. Fusion of the mixed nitrates followed by leaching with water rapidly concentrates yttrium in the more basic fractions and effects its separation from the heavier lanthanides. The procedure is effective where oxidation can occur (e.g., with Ce or Pr, p. 65) but not in most other cases.

Ion Exchange. The exchange of metal ions in solution with protons on a solid ion exchanger is an equilibrium process

$$M^{n+} + nHR\,(s) \rightleftharpoons M\,(R)_n(s) + nH^+$$

where HR represents an exchange point on a hydrogen-cycle resin. Similarly, one metal ion may exchange for another

$$M'^{n+} + M(R)_n(s) \rightleftharpoons M'(R)_n(s) + M^{n+}$$

This process is familiar in the exchange of calcium ion for sodium ion in water softening.

Observation that the tenacity with which a cation is held by an ion exchanger decreases with its crystal radius and charge, as

$$Th^{4+} > La^{3+} > Ce^{3+} > Y^{3+} > Lu^{3+} > Ba^{2+} >$$
$$Ca^{2+} > K^+ > NH_4^+ > H^+$$

suggested separation of the lanthanides by an exchange process. However, the pioneering studies of D. W. Pearce and R. G. Russell at Purdue University showed that when several tripositive lanthanides were adsorbed on an exchanger, their removal by adding sodium chloride effected no greater degree of separation than conventional fractional crystallization or precipitation. On the other hand, observation at Oak Ridge, Tennessee, that niobium and zirconium could be removed selectively from an ion exchange column with oxalic acid solution suggested that separation of the lanthanides might be similarly effected by elution with appropriate complexing agents.

Extensive tracer-scale experiments, carried out largely under the supervision of G. E. Boyd and E. R. Tompkins at Oak Ridge and first reported publicly in 1947, showed that if the mixed tripositive lanthanides are adsorbed as a band at the top of a cation exchange column and then eluted with a suitable complexing agent (e.g., buffered citric acid solution), separation of the cations into individual bands occurs on the column, and the species ultimately leave the column in reverse order of their atomic numbers. This is shown in Fig. 4.2, where the fractionation of 0.01–0.1 mg. quantities shows an elution peak for each ion in question. The use of such data in establishing the existence of element 61 (Pm) has been discussed in Chapter 1 (p. 8).

1. *Ion Exchange Equilibria and the Significance of Complexing Agents.* In order that subsequent developments may be both understandable and logical, we must now show why the

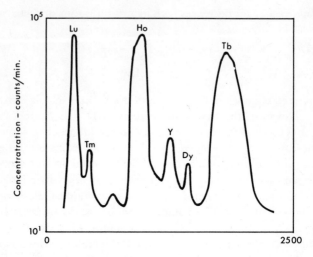

Fig. 4.2. Tracer-scale elution with 5% citrate at pH 3.20. (Redrawn from Ketelle, B. H., and Boyd, G. E., *J. Am. Chem. Soc.* **69**, 2800 (1947).)

fractionating ability of an exchanger is enhanced by a complexing agent.

The distribution of a lanthanide between a solid exchanger (r) and an aqueous phase (aq) in terms of the equilibrium (p. 80).

$$Ln^{3+}(aq) + 3HR(s) \rightleftharpoons Ln(R)_3(s) + 3H^+(aq)$$

is described as

$$\lambda_0 = c_{Ln^{3+}(r)}/c_{Ln^{3+}(aq)} \qquad (4.4)$$

where λ_0 is a distribution coefficient. Neglecting ionic charges for convenience gives

$$\lambda_0 = c_{Ln(r)}/c_{Ln(aq)} \qquad (4.5)$$

For a second lanthanide (Ln'), we have similarly

$$\lambda'_0 = c_{Ln'(r)} / c_{Ln'(aq)} \qquad (4.6)$$

and the separation factor (p. 74) then becomes

$$\alpha = \lambda'_0 / \lambda_0 = c_{Ln'(r)} c_{Ln(aq)} / c_{Ln(r)} c_{Ln'(aq)} \qquad (4.7)$$

Under the conditions described, the value of α seldom departs significantly from unity.

If now a chelating agent (p. 54) is introduced, the additional equilibria (p. 55)

$$Ln + n(AA) \rightleftharpoons Ln(AA)_n$$

and

$$Ln' + n(AA) \rightleftharpoons Ln'(AA)_n$$

are established in solution. Inasmuch as the total concentration of either lanthanide in solution is the sum of the complexed and uncomplexed material, the distribution between resin and solution (for Ln as typical) is modified to

$$\lambda = c_{Ln(r)} / (c_{Ln(aq)} + c_{Ln(AA)_n(aq)}) \qquad (4.8)$$

The expression for the formation constant for the chelated species (Eq. 3.1, p. 55) can be solved to give

$$c_{Ln(AA)_n(aq)} = K_{Ln(AA)_n} c_{Ln(aq)} c^n_{AA(aq)} \qquad (4.9)$$

which upon substitution in Eq. 4.8 yields

$$\lambda = c_{Ln(r)} / c_{Ln(aq)} (1 + K_{Ln(AA)_n} c^n_{AA(aq)}) \qquad (4.10)$$

Then substitution of the relationship in Eq. 4.4 gives

$$\lambda = \lambda_0 / (1 + K_{Ln(AA)_n} c^n_{AA(aq)}) \qquad (4.11)$$

which, if the formation constant is sufficiently large, reduces to

$$\lambda = \lambda_0 / K_{Ln(AA)_n} c^n_{AA(aq)} \qquad (4.12)$$

Equation 4.12 indicates how distribution between resin and solution phases is affected by the stability of the complex species. Quite obviously, the behavior of Ln' would be similarly described in terms of $K'_{Ln'(AA)_n}$.

Under these circumstances, we may then define a new separation factor as

$$\alpha = \lambda'/\lambda \qquad (4.13)$$

which in terms of Eq. 4.12 and its equivalent for Ln' and simplification becomes

$$\alpha = \lambda'_0 K_{Ln(AA)_n}/\lambda_0 K'_{Ln'(AA)_n} \qquad (4.14)$$

Thus if the chelating agent gives complex species of different stability with two (or more) cations, the ability of a resin to separate these ions is markedly enhanced. The feasibility of separating the lanthanides in this way is apparent from the trends in stability of complex species already discussed (pp. 57, 60).

These considerations are simplest when but a single complex species formed as a result of reaction of the cation with the ligand in a 1:1 mole ratio results. Although this is generally true of the amine polycarboxylates (pp. 57, 60), it is not true of the citrates, where several compositions, depending upon pH, are possible. It is assumed in these discussions, of course, that the chelated species are of sufficient stability that the concentration of an uncomplexed cation in solution is negligible in comparison with that of the complex species and that the pH is sufficiently high that equilibria of the type

$$Ln(AA)_n^{m-} + H^+ \rightleftharpoons HLn(AA)_n^{(m-)+1}$$

can be neglected.

Elution of adsorbed ions thus involves the successive steps of removal from the resin as the complexed species and redeposition from that species further down the column. Inasmuch as both equilibria are controlled by the stability of the chelated species, separation of the cations into individual bands ultimately occurs. The ideal requirements that each band be sharply defined and that overlap between adjacent bands be minimized necessitate rapid and essentially complete constraining reactions at

a. The front of the band, where the *retaining ion* on the unused exchanger must permit redeposition of the Ln^{3+} ion from solution and simultaneous removal of the chelating agent in soluble form. The retaining ion may be hydrogen ion or a metal ion that gives more stable chelated species than the lanthanides (p. 57).

b. The rear of the band, where the complexing agent must remove the lanthanides from the exchanger.

2. *Macro Separations by Ion Exchange.* Adaptation of these techniques to a macro scale was due largely to the work of F. H. Spedding, J. E. Powell, and their collaborators at the Iowa State University laboratories. It was found that the 5% ammonium citrate system at pH 2.5–3.2 which proved effective on a tracer scale so spread each lanthanide throughout a macro column that extensive overlapping of the characteristic bell-shaped elution curves (Fig. 4.2) could be avoided only by excessive increase in column length. Use of 0.1% ammonium citrate at pH 5.0–8.0, where only the species $[Ln(cit)_2]^{3-}$ is significant, however, effected rapid separation with the development of sharply defined rectangular bands of minimum overlap (Fig. 4.3). Both constraining reactions were rapid and complete, and hydrogen ion proved to be a suitable retaining ion. This system was used to separate kilogram quantities of lanthanides of better than 99.99% purity, but its low total capacity renders it commercially unattractive.

Experimental observations that the aminepolycarboxylates give over wide pH ranges 1:1 chelates of both greater stability and larger differences in stability between adjacent lantha-

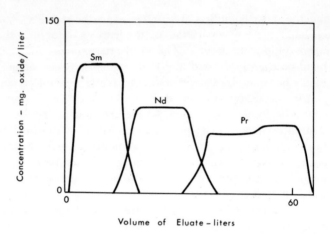

Fig. 4.3. Macro-scale elution with 0.1% citrate at pH 5.30. (Redrawn from Spedding, F. H., Fulmer, E. I., Powell, J. E., and Butler, T. A., *J. Am. Chem. Soc.* **72**, 2354 (1950).)

nides (Table 3.11) and are useful at larger concentrations directed attention to these reagents. All of the early investigations and much of the current practice have involved ethylenediaminetetraacetate (p. 56). For this chelating agent, an average separation factor of 2.38 for adjacent lanthanides is observed.

Initially it was shown that when a binary mixture (e.g., Nd^{3+} and Er^{3+}) was treated with insufficient ethylenediaminetetraacetate to tie up all the ions and then passed through an ammonium-cycle exchanger, the more basic cation (Nd^{3+}) was retained, and the less basic (Er^{3+}) passed through. This *differential filter* behavior of the exchanger resulted in gross separations but direct substitution of ethylenediaminetetraacetate for citrate in elution procedures involving hydrogen ion as a retaining species resulted in precipitation of the free acid H_4EDTA and certain of the hydrogen chelates $H[Ln(EDTA)] \cdot xH_2O$. However, use of a suitable metal ion as a retainer obviates this problem. Copper(II) ion has been used most successfully. It does not yield precipitates under optimum pH conditions, and it elutes with the Yb^{3+} and Lu^{3+} ions. The latter is a consequence of the fact that although the formation constant of the copper(II)–EDTA chelate is less than that of the erbium chelate, the more highly charged lanthanides are held more tenaciously by the exchanger. The lanthanides separate in the order of their formation constants (Table 3.11), with yttrium appearing between terbium and dysprosium.

Data for a typical Cu^{2+}–$EDTA^{4-}$ system are summarized in Table 4.4. In practice, columns several feet in diameter and many feet in height and with capacities of hundreds of pounds are used routinely by all large-scale producers.

Other chelating agents may be used to advantage. Both the acids H_3HEDTA and H_5DTPA (Table 3.10) permit the rapid recovery of yttrium by concentrating this element with

TABLE 4.4. Ion Exchange Separation of Neodymium from Praseodymium with EDTA and Cu^{2+} Retaining Ion at pH 7.97[*]

Sample		Ln_2O_3 recovered, g.	Pr_6O_{11}, %	Nd_2O_3, %
Original		11.6194	50	50
Fraction	1	0.4126	<0.08	>99.9
	2	0.9584	<0.08	>99.9
	3	0.9519	<0.08	>99.9
	4	0.9867	<0.08	>99.9
	5	0.9575	<0.08	>99.9
	6	0.9453	11	88
	7	0.9400	64	34
	8	0.9283	96	4
	9	0.9213	>99.9	0.1
	10	0.9156	>99.9	<0.06
	11	0.9122	>99.9	<0.06
	12	0.9167	>99.9	<0.06
	13	0.6265	>99.9	<0.06

[*] Data from Spedding, F. H., Powell, J. E., and Wheelwright, E. J., *J. Am. Chem. Soc.* **76,** 2557 (1954)

the cerium group. Inasmuch as neither reagent is precipitated by acid, the proton is a useful retaining ion in these systems. The α-hydroxycarboxylates (lactate, hydroxybutyrate) are also efficient for macro separations. The reagent H_4DCTA is similar to H_4EDTA, but the enhanced stabilities of its chelates increase the time necessary for separations. Increased temperatures result in more rapid separations.

3. *Anion Exchange.* At the present, this approach is useful only for the removal of thorium (p. 73).

Solvent Extraction. The pioneering work of W. Fischer and his associates at Hannover (reported in 1937) showing small differences in distribution of the trichlorides between water and partially miscible alcohols, ketones, or ethers gave little promise for easy separations but established a foundation for future success. Highly significant was J. C. Warf's observation (1949) that cerium(IV) can be readily and completely separated from the tripositive cations by extraction from an aqueous nitric acid solution into tri-*n*-butyl phosphate (p. 73). The importance of this type of system for the separation of the tripositive species from each other was first emphasized in 1953 by D. F. Peppard and his collaborators at the Argonne National Laboratory. This was followed in the same year by the isolation of the "first kilogram" of pure gadolinium by B. Weaver and his co-workers at the Oak Ridge National Laboratory using the same procedure. Subsequently the method has been used on both tracer and macro scales.

1. *Tri-n-butyl Phosphate Extractions.* It is generally agreed that in nitrate medium, where extractions with tri-*n*-butyl phosphate (TBP) are most effective, an equilibrium of the type

$$Ln^{3+}(aq) + 3NO_3^-(aq) + 3TBP(org) \rightleftharpoons$$

$$Ln(NO_3)_3(TBP)_3(org)$$

where (org) represents the nonaqueous phase, is established. Distribution between the two phases is then described as

$$\lambda = c_{Ln(NO_3)_3(TBP)_3(org)} / c_{Ln^{3+}(aq)} \qquad (4.15)$$

and for two lanthanides, the separation factor becomes

$$\alpha = \lambda' / \lambda$$
$$= c_{Ln'(NO_3)_3(TBP)_3(org)} c_{Ln^{3+}(aq)} / c_{Ln(NO_3)_3(TBP)_3(org)} c_{Ln'^{3+}(aq)} \qquad (4.16)$$

Peppard reported an average separation factor of ca. 1.5 for adjacent lanthanides for $15.8M$ nitric acid–100% TBP systems.

Such a distribution equilibrium is described as

$$K = c_{Ln(NO_3)_3(TBP)_3(org)} / c_{Ln^{3+}(aq)} c^3_{NO_3^-(aq)} c^3_{TBP(org)} \qquad (4.17)$$

Combination of this expression with Eq. 4.15 and simplification gives

$$\lambda = K c^3_{NO_3^-(aq)} c^3_{TBP(org)} \qquad (4.18)$$

If this equilibrium is the correct one, a plot of $\log_{10}\lambda$ vs. $c_{NO_3^-}$ at constant c_{TBP} should be a straight line with slope 3. That this is indeed the case above nitric acid concentrations of ca. $10M$ is shown in Fig. 4.4. This figure also indicates that, as we might expect, extent of extraction increases with decreasing crystal radius. Yttrium appears at $Z = 67$–68. The regularity is such that Eq. 4.16 can be reduced to

$$\log_{10}\lambda = Z \log \alpha + \text{constant} \qquad (4.19)$$

2. *Di(2-ethylhexyl)phosphoric Acid Extractions.* This reagent is both more resistant to hydrolytic decomposition in contact with aqueous nitric acid than TBP and a more efficient extractant. An average separation factor of 2.5 for adjacent lanthanides has been reported.

Esters of this type (HDGP) exist as dimers in the non-aqueous phase. Extraction apparently involves the equilibrium

$$Ln^{3+}(aq) + 3(HDGP)_2(org) \rightleftharpoons$$
$$Ln[H(DGP)_2]_3(org) + 3H^+(aq)$$

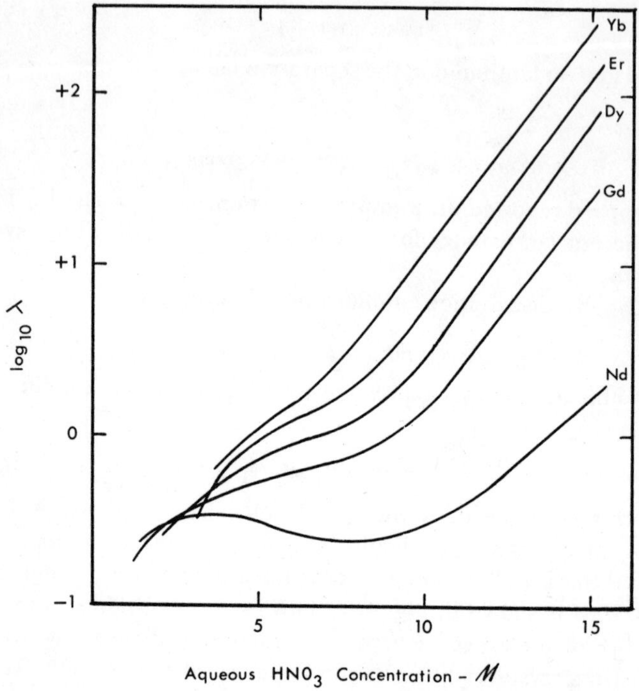

Fig. 4.4. Extraction of tripositive ions with 100% TBP. (Redrawn in part from Hesford, E., Jackson, E. E., and McKay, H. A. C., *J. Inorg. Nucl. Chem.* **9,** 279 (1950).)

from which a distribution ratio

$$\lambda = K c^3_{(HDGP)_2(org)} / c^3_{H^+(aq)} \qquad (4.20)$$

can be derived. The experimentally determined distribution ratio for a given lanthanide does indeed depend upon $c^3_{(HDGP)_2(org)}$ and $1/c^3_{H^+(aq)}$. It is believed that esters of this type form chelates in which units of the type

$$RO\diagdown_{P}\diagup^{O--H---O}\diagdown_{P}\diagup^{OR}$$
$$RO\diagup\diagdown O\qquad O\diagdown^{OR}$$
$$Ln/3$$

where R is an alkyl group, exist.

3. *Other Extractions.* Less success has been achieved with monoalkylphosphoric acids, $RP(O)(OH)_2$; pyrophosphate esters, $(RO)_2P(O)-O-P(O)(OR)_2$; phosphonates, $(RO)_2(R)PO$ and $(RO)(R)P(O)(OH)$; 1,3-diketones; or 8-quinolinols. Amines (p. 71) are not useful.

4. *Present Status of Solvent Extraction.* Although solvent extraction is promising as a general method and lends itself to continuous operation with a minimum of attention, it is not yet competitive with ion exchange as a general method for separation. Its major uses are in the purification of cerium (p. 73), thorium (p. 71), and lanthanum. Lanthanum is somewhat less readily extracted than the other tripositive ions and can thus be freed from them rather readily. Scandium is easily separated and purified by solvent extraction with tri-*n*-butyl phosphate or diethyl ether.

Selective Oxidation or Reduction. Previous discussions of the nontripositive oxidation states (pp. 17–19, 43–46, 60–66, 80) have provided sufficient information so that only a few additional comments are necessary. Inasmuch as change of oxidation state is accompanied by a profound change in properties, selective oxidation or reduction provides a remarkably clean and efficient way of separating specific lanthanides.

1. *Oxidation to the Tetrapositive State.* Practical separations are limited to the removal of cerium after oxidation (p. 73).

2. *Reduction to the Dipositive State.* Only the reduction of europium(III) with zinc, followed by its recovery as the divalent sulfate or chloride, is useful. In practice, it is possible to recover europium from mixtures containing only trace

quantities by adding zinc dust, barium chloride, and sulfuric acid and oxidizing the mixed barium–europium(II) sulfate precipitate (procedure of· H. N. McCoy). This is often a better approach than ion exchange.

3. *Reduction to Amalgams.* Europium, samarium, and ytterbium are readily removed from mixtures either by extracting a buffered acidic solution with liquid sodium amalgam (J. K. Marsh) or by electrolyzing an alkaline citrate solution with a lithium amalgam cathode (E. I. Onstott). Other lanthanides can be separated less readily in this way. The sodium amalgam procedure is convenient·and rapid; the electrolytic one can be operated continuously and on a large scale. Modification of each permits separation of the individual elements.

Physical Methods. Differences in volatility of the anhydrous halides at elevated temperature, in speed of ionic migration in solution, in thermal or other types of diffusion in solution, or in attraction by a strong magnetic field have all been suggested as bases for separation. None of these has proved practical, although the first is promising.

Applications of the Lanthanides

Quite arbitrarily, these may be classified as (1) metals and alloys, (2) nonnuclear uses of compounds, and (3) nuclear applications.

Metals and Alloys. Roughly one-fourth of the production of lanthanides is used in this way. The pure metals have little use in their own right, but alloys (known as mischmetals) containing predominantly cerium (30–50%), together with smaller quantities of the other cerium group metals·and nonlanthanide impurities,[*] have sufficiently strong reducing power for metallurgical applications. Mischmetal is an excellent scavenger for oxygen or sulfur in many metal systems.

[*] A typical mischmetal contains 45–50% Ce, 22–25% La, 18% Nd, 5% Pr, 1% Sm, and smaller amounts of other lanthanides.

Magnesium alloys containing ca. 3% mischmetal and 1% zirconium have sufficiently high strength and creep resistance at 450–600°F. to be useful in jet engine parts. Mischmetal imparts high-temperature strength to aluminum, oxidation resistance to nickel alloys, hardness to copper, and workability to stainless steel and vanadium. When alloyed with ca. 30% iron, it is sufficiently pyrophoric to be useful in lighter flints. Both mischmetal and yttrium have a marked nodulizing effect upon graphite and thus enhance the malleability of cast iron.

Compounds—Nonnuclear Applications.   Ceramic and related applications consume about one-fourth of the lanthanides produced. Another fourth, as fluorides, appears in cored carbons for improvement of intensity and color balance in arc lights.

1. *Ceramic Applications.*   These include cerium(IV) oxide and cerium-rich (> 40% CeO_2) oxide mixtures as highly efficient glass-polishing compositions; neodymium and praseodymium oxides as coloring agents for glass and in the production of standard filters (p. 32); lanthanum oxide in the preparation of low-dispersion, high-refraction optical glass; cerium(IV) oxide to improve the stability and discoloration resistance of glass to gamma or electron-beam radiation; cerium(IV) and neodymium oxides to counteract the iron(II)-produced green in glass; ca. 3% praseodymium oxide in combination with zirconium(IV) oxide to give a yellow ceramic glaze; and cerium(IV) oxide to opacify in enamels. The high melting points of the oxides, certain sulfides (e.g., CeS), borides, carbides, and nitrides suggest their use as refractories, although at least some of these are reactive at high temperatures.

2. *Catalytic Applications.*   Known uses of these compounds as catalysts include the oxides in the hydrogenation, dehydrogenation, and oxidation of various organic compounds;

the anhydrous chlorides in polyesterification processes; and the chlorides and cerium phosphate in petroleum cracking. In the sense that heterogeneous catalysts are commonly characterized by unpaired electrons, paramagnetism, defect structures, or variability in oxidation state, catalysis is a promising practical area.

3. *Magnetic and Electronic Applications.* Industry has been slow in taking advantage of the para- and ferromagnetic properties of the lanthanides. The low electrical and eddy-current losses of the ferrimagnetic garnets, $3Ln_2O_3 \cdot 5Fe_2O_3$, make these substances useful in microwave devices and as magnetic core materials. The yttrium compound (so-called "yig") is particularly important. Certain compounds (e.g., selenides, tellurides) are of potential interest as semiconductors or thermoelectrics. The titanates and stannates, as a consequence of large dielectric constants and small temperature coefficients of capacitance, are useful ceramic capacitors.

Nuclear Applications. These include actual and potential uses of high-cross-section metals or compounds (p. 37) in control, shielding, and flux-suppressing devices; of hydrides (especially of yttrium) as hydrogen-moderator carriers; of oxides as diluents in nuclear fuels; of metals for structural components (e.g., yttrium pipe that is not attacked by molten 5% Cr–95% U at 1000° C.) or structural-alloy-modifying components (e.g., scavengers) of reactors; of coprecipitants of fission-product poisons (e.g., high-cross-section ^{149}Sm) in molten fluoride fuels; and of suitably irradiated materials as portable X-ray sources (e.g., Tm) or as radiation sources (e.g., Eu).

The Possibilities. Extensive uses of the lanthanides have always been limited by commercial scarcity and high cost. The problems of availability have not been solved completely, but they have been reduced substantially. Costs have decreased almost exponentially since the development of ion exchange techniques. As continuing research reveals new and unique potentialities, costs may be expected to decrease until ultimately they will reach levels where the lanthanides can become competitive with some of the more common elements.

And Now, What Remains?

Thus we conclude our treatment of the chemistry of the lanthanides. If, in presenting this account, we have both answered some of your questions about this interesting series of elements and simultaneously raised some additional ones in your mind, we shall consider our efforts useful. One task remains—to clarify some of our allusions to the actinides as another series of closely related elements, the chemistry of which has rendered that of the lanthanides no longer completely unique. This we do, but with apologies for necessary brevity, in the next chapter.

Selected Readings

Kremers, H. E., "Rare Metals Handbook," C. A. Hampel, Ed., ch. 19, Reinhold Publishing Corp., New York, 1961. (Technology, applications.)

Little, H. F. V., "A Text-book of Inorganic Chemistry," J. N. Friend, Ed., Vol. IV., 2nd ed., ch. X, Charles Griffin and Co., London, 1921. (Occurrence, recovery, classical separations.)

Spedding, F. H., and Daane, A. H., Eds., "The Rare Earths," John Wiley & Sons, New York, 1961. (Fractional crystallization, ch. 3; solvent extraction, ch. 4; ion exchange, ch. 5; applications, chs. 19–22; analysis, chs. 23, 24.)

Vickery, R. C., "Chemistry of the Lanthanons," Academic Press, New York, 1953. (Occurrence, recovery, separations, uses.)

Vickery, R. C., "Analytical Chemistry of the Rare Earths," Pergamon Press, London, 1961.

Yost, D. M., Russell, H., Jr., and Garner, C. S., "The Rare-Earth Elements and Their Compounds," ch. 5, John Wiley & Sons, New York, 1947. (Separations.)

chapter five

THE ACTINIDES—
A RELATED SERIES FOR
SCIENTIFIC PIONEERING

Prior to 1940, there was apparently every reason to believe that electronic configurations based upon f orbitals were unique to the lanthanides. No element heavier than uranium had been positively identified, and the properties of the heaviest of the known elements (Ac, Th, Pa, U) seemed to resemble those of the d-type transition metals of Periodic Groups IIIb–VIb (i.e., La, Hf, Ta, W) sufficiently to permit classification in these groups. Although it is true that some apparent anomalies in magnetic and spectroscopic properties, particularly of uranium compounds, had prompted theoretical speculation as to the possible existence of a second lanthanide-type, or $5f$, series, experimental support was lacking. Indeed, what seemed to be the only support of this type—namely, the postulation by E. Fermi that the multiplicity of β^- activities obtained when uranium is bombarded with slow neutrons indicates the formation of transuranium species—vanished when, in 1939, O. Hahn and F. Strassmann associated these activities with well-known lighter elements produced by neutron-induced fission.

In 1940, E. M. McMillan and P. Abelson proved conclusively that a nuclide with a half-life of 2.3 days, which remained in natural uranium after fission of the 235 isotope, was not a lanthanide. Rather, it was a new species resembling the lanthanides in a lower oxidation state and uranium (as UO_2^{2+} ion) in a higher state but differing significantly from each. This was neptunium (from the planet Neptune), the first of the true transuranium elements, formed as a consequence of the reaction sequence[*]

$$^{238}_{92}U + ^{1}_{0}n \longrightarrow ^{239}_{92}U + \gamma$$
$$^{239}_{92}U \underset{23 \text{ min.}}{\longrightarrow} ^{239}_{93}Np + \beta^-$$

The discovery of plutonium (from Pluto) by G. T. Seaborg, E. M. McMillan, J. W. Kennedy, and A. C. Wahl later in 1940 as a result of the sequence

$$^{238}_{92}U(d, 2n)^{238}_{93}Np \xrightarrow[2.1 \text{ days}]{-\beta^-} ^{238}_{94}Pu$$

and the subsequent identification of the important 239 isotope in 1941 by the same group in collaboration with E. Segrè as the decay product of neptunium-239 laid the basis for work that has now given us elements with atomic numbers through 103 (Lw). Much of this work was done at the University of California under the able direction of G. T. Seaborg.

---

[*] These nuclear reactions are described more concisely by the notation

$$^{238}_{92}U(n,\gamma)^{239}_{92}U \xrightarrow[23 \text{ min.}]{-\beta^-} ^{239}_{93}Np$$

The Actinide Hypothesis

Intensive chemical studies involving both the newly isolated transuranium species and the elements Ac–U revealed many similarities to the lanthanides, similarities that had not been previously suspected in the actinium–uranium region and similarities that became increasingly striking with increase in atomic number. Indeed, among the heavier species, these were sufficient that the known chemistry of the lanthanides proved invaluable in predicting behaviors and reactions. With the addition of evidence from magnetic and spectroscopic data for the presence of f electrons, Seaborg was prompted to postulate that the elements following actinium are members of a second inner or f-type transition series, a so-called *actinide* series.

The significance of this postulation is indicated by the ease with which it brought order into this developing chemistry and permitted the correlation of both chemical and physical data. Its weakness and major point of criticism are merely that implied similarities to the lanthanides are not always exact. Prominent among observed differences is the tendency of the actinides to show a greater multiplicity of oxidation states with perhaps a greater over-all preference for the tetrapositive state over the tripositive. As was shown for the lanthanides (pp. 17, 19), however, the existence of a particular and common oxidation state of any magnitude is a consequence of an appropriate combination of properties and is in no way as important as similarities and differences in data that reflect electronic arrangements.

For our purposes, it is sufficient to know that the heavy elements do resemble the lanthanides very closely and to explore these similarities in terms of the principles and observations we have developed for the lanthanides. Our exploration can thus be handled more logically on a general basis than as a highly detailed discussion.

Electronic Configurations

The difficulties encountered in assigning ground-state configurations to the lanthanides are even more acute with the actinides. Furthermore, the increasing nuclear instability of the latter with increasing atomic number seriously limits experimental studies. The configurations summarized in Table 5.1 are considered to be the most probable in terms of presently available data. Comparison of these with the corresponding ones for the lanthanides (Table 2.1) shows both a substantial over-all similarity and an enhanced tendency for the lighter members (Ac–Np) to retain d electrons. The latter tendency results both from the even smaller energy separation between the $6d$ and $5f$ orbitals than that already mentioned for the $5d$ and $4f$ orbitals and from the difference in change in binding energy of the most readily removable $6d$ and $5f$ electrons with atomic number, as shown qualitatively in Fig. 5.1. Where the series starts is thus somewhat of an academic question.

The configurations associated with the various oxidation states, as was true with the lanthanides (Table 2.2), show a generally greater regularity. There is a discernible preference for the $5f^0$ and $5f^7$ configurations (compare p. 19). Again, constancy of a given state is less closely related to electronic configuration than to ionization energy, hydration energy, and lattice energy (p. 18), but the more extensive spatial projection of the $5f$ orbitals into the "outer" or valence regions of these atoms reduces the shielding of these electrons, renders them easier to remove, and increases the number of observed oxidation states. The relative stabilities of these states in aqueous solution, where known, are shown by the oxidation potential data in Table 5.2.

TABLE 5.1. Electronic Configurations of the Actinides

Atomic number	Name	Symbol	Configuration in oxidation state				
			0	+3	+4	+5	+6
89	Actinium	Ac	$6d^17s^2$	$5f^0$			
90	Thorium	Th	$6d^27s^2$	—	$5f^0$		
91	Protactinium	Pa	$5f^26d^17s^2$	—	$5f^1$	$5f^0$	
92	Uranium	U	$5f^36d^17s^2$	$5f^3$	$5f^2$	$5f^1$	$5f^0$
93	Neptunium	Np	$5f^46d^17s^2$	$5f^4$	$5f^3$	$5f^2$	$5f^1$
94	Plutonium	Pu	$5f^67s^2$	$5f^5$	$5f^4$	$5f^3$	$5f^2$
95	Americium	Am	$5f^77s^2$	$5f^6$	$5f^5$	$5f^4$	$5f^3$
96	Curium	Cm	$5f^76d^17s^2$	$5f^7$	$5f^6$		
97	Berkelium	Bk	$5f^97s^2$	$5f^8$			
98	Californium	Cf	$5f^{10}7s^2$	$5f^9$			
99	Einsteinium	Es	$5f^{11}7s^2$	$5f^{10}$			
100	Fermium	Fm	$5f^{12}7s^2$	$5f^{11}$			
101	Mendelevium	Md	$5f^{13}7s^2$	$5f^{12}$			
102	Nobelium*	No	$5f^{14}7s^2$	$5f^{13}$			
103	Lawrencium	Lw	$5f^{14}6d^17s^2$	$5f^{14}$			

* Name not completely accepted.

TABLE 5.2. Some Characteristics of Ionic Species

Symbol	Oxidation-reduction in acidic media		Crystal radius, Å		Light absorption in aqueous solution		
	Couple	E°_{298}, * v.	+3	+4	Ion	Color	Wave length, Å
Ac	Ac^0-Ac^{3+}	(2.6)	1.11		Ac^{3+}	Colorless	None
Th	Th^0-Th^{4+}	1.90	(1.08)	0.99	Th^{4+}	Colorless	None
Pa	$Pa^0-PaO_2^+$	(1.0)	(1.05)	0.96	Pa^{4+}	Colorless	2240, 2550, 2760
U	U^0-U^{3+}	1.80	1.03	0.93	U^{3+}	Reddish	5200, 8800, 9000
	$U^{3+}-U^{4+}$	0.631			U^{4+}	Green	5500, 6500
	$U^{4+}-UO_2^+$	−0.58			UO_2^{2+}	Yellow	4000, 4110, 4250
	$UO_2^+-UO_2^{2+}$	−0.063					
Np	Np^0-Np^{3+}	1.83	1.01		Np^{3+}	Violet	5520, 6610, 7875
	$Np^{3+}-Np^{4+}$	−0.155		0.92	Np^{4+}	Yellow-green	5040, 7430, 8250
	$Np^{4+}-NpO_2^+$	−0.739			NpO_2^{2+}	Pink	4760, 5570
	$NpO_2^+-NpO_2^{2+}$	−1.137					
Pu	Pu^0-Pu^{3+}	2.03	1.00		Pu^{3+}	Deep blue	5600, 6000, 6030
	$Pu^{3+}-Pu^{4+}$	−0.982		0.90	Pu^{4+}	Tan	4700, 6550, 8150
	$Pu^{4+}-PuO_2^+$	−1.172			PuO_2^{2+}	Yellow-orange	8330, 9530, 9830
	$PuO_2^+-PuO_2^{2+}$	−0.913					
Am	Am^0-Am^{3+}	2.32	0.99	0.89	Am^{3+}	Pink	5027, 8200
	$Am^{3+}-AmO_2^+$	−1.74			AmO_2^+	Yellow	5131, 7151
	$AmO_2^+-AmO_2^{2+}$	−1.60			AmO_2^{2+}	Brownish	6660, 9950
Cm	—	—	—	—	Cm^{3+}	Colorless	2368, 2680, 2774

* Estimated values in parentheses.

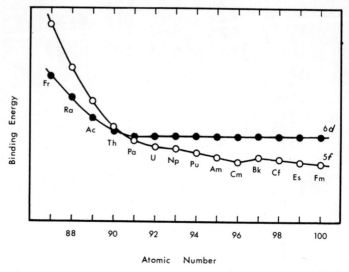

Fig. 5.1. Qualitative comparison of binding energies of 5*f* and 6*d* electrons. (Redrawn from Katz, J. J., and Seaborg, G. T., *The Chemistry of the Actinide Elements*, p. 465, Metheun, London, 1957.)

Magnetic and Light Absorption Characteristics

It is apparent from Fig. 5.2 that the magnetic effects resulting from unpaired 5*f* electrons are closely comparable to those associated with the 4*f* electrons in the lanthanides (p. 27). It is thus reasonable to conclude that the origins of these effects are similar. It must be pointed out, however, that not all data for the actinides show this parallel and that those used in constructing Fig. 5.2 have been selected rather deliberately. Decrease in the shielding of the 5*f* electrons makes these electrons more susceptible to enviromental influences than the 4*f* electrons (p. 28) and thus eliminates the constancy of moment for a given oxidation state that characterizes the lanthanides.

Parallels in the influence of *f* electrons upon light absorption

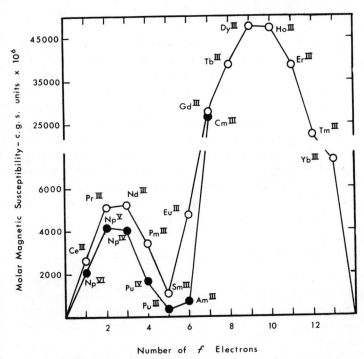

Fig. 5.2. Comparison of magnetic susceptibilities of lanthanide and actinide species. (Redrawn from Katz and Seaborg, *op. cit.*, p. 447.)

are apparent from a comparison of the data on actinide species (Table 5.2) with those for the lanthanides (Table 2.7). Species with the same number of f electrons often have roughly comparable spectra, e.g., Ce^{3+} and Pa^{4+} (f^1), Nd^{3+} and U^{3+} (f^3), Gd^{3+} and Cm^{3+} (f^7). In a number of instances, the absorption peaks of the actinides are even more sharply defined than those of the lanthanides. However, as is true of magnetic moments, light absorption is much more affected by environment than with the lanthanides.

Crystal Radius

In a given oxidation state, the actinide ions (Table 5.2) are only slightly larger than the analogous lanthanide ions (Table 2.4). It is not surprising, therefore, to find many instances of isomorphism among compounds between the two series. This is used to practical advantage when a lanthanide carries trace quantities of an actinide in a separation or a reaction. The expected actinide contraction produces the same general trends in properties as noted for the lanthanides (p. 24). Important among these are variations in the solution stabilities of complex ions. Such ions are more common and more stable than those of the lanthanides because of the greater availability of the $5f$ orbitals for bond formation.

Some Additional Similarities, Differences, and Information

Although it is true that the actinides are so closely related to the lanthanides that much of what we have learned in Chapters 2–4 can be extrapolated to the $5f$ series, detailed studies have shown this to be somewhat less permissible with the lighter actinides than with the heavier ones. It seems logical, therefore, to subdivide the series rather than to attempt an all-inclusive discussion in presenting our concluding comments. This approach derives support also from the fact that only the elements Ac–U occur in nature in sufficient quantity to permit their recovery in ponderable amounts. Although both neptunium and plutonium (in particular) are undeniably present in uranium minerals as a result of natural fission processes, what we know about the transuranium elements is based entirely upon synthetically produced materials. As a prelude to the summary that follows, comparison of the numerical data in Table 5.3 with comparable data for the lanthanides (Table 3.1) will be useful.

TABLE 5.3.   Numerical Constants of the Actinides

Symbol	Atomic weight*	Natural isotopes	Density,† g./cm.^{3}	Melting point, °C.	Boiling point (approx.), °C.
Ac	(227)	227, 228	—	1050	—
Th	232.038	227, 228, 230, 231, 232, 234	11.72	1750	3500–4200
Pa	(231)	231, 234	15.37	—	—
U	238.04	234, 235, 238	19.04	1132	3818
Np	(237)	239	19.5	640	—
Pu	(242)	239	19.82	639.5	3235
Am	(243)	None	11.7	1100	—
Cm	(247)	None	7	—	—
Bk	(247)	None	—	—	—
Cf	(251)	None	—	—	—
Es	(254)	None	—	—	—
Fm	(253)	None	—	—	—
Md	(256)	None	—	—	—
No	(254)	None	—	—	—
Lw	—	None	—	—	—

* Longest-lived isotope in parentheses; others based upon ^{12}C = 12.0000.
† Of stable modification at room temperature.

The Actinium–Uranium Elements.   The natural abundances of these elements in the igneous rocks of the crust of the earth (Ac, $3 \times 10^{-14}\%$; Th, $1.15 \times 10^{-3}\%$; Pa, $8 \times 10^{-11}\%$; U, $4 \times 10^{-4}\%$) indicate that although thorium and uranium compare in potential availability with such elements as zinc, arsenic, or tungsten, actinium and protactinium are among our scarcest elements. All known isotopes of these elements are radioactive. It is only because the half-lives of their important natural isotopes ($^{232}_{90}Th$, $^{235}_{92}U$, $^{238}_{92}U$) are of the same order of magnitude as the age of the earth (p. 9) that thorium and uranium have persisted to the present. The half-lives of even the most stable actinium ($^{227}_{89}Ac$, 22 years) and protactinium ($^{231}_{91}Pa$, 3.4×10^4 years) isotopes are so short, however, that these elements exist only because they are continuously regenerated as members of the uranium-235 decay series.

The occurrence and recovery of thorium have been discussed (pp. 69, 71). Uranium materials are concentrated from the pitchblendes (U_3O_8, found in Central Africa, Canada, Soviet Russia) and carnotites ($KUO_2VO_4 \cdot 1.5H_2O$, found in the southwestern United States) and separated by solvent extraction or precipitation (commonly as $(NH_4)_2U_2O_7$). Final purification is by solvent extraction. Inasmuch as only minute quantities of actinium or protactinium can be obtained from uranium minerals or process residues, these elements are more conveniently obtained (in gram quantities) as products of the reaction sequences

$$^{226}_{88}\text{Ra}(n, \gamma)\,^{227}_{88}\text{Ra} \xrightarrow[\text{41.2 min.}]{-\beta^-} \,^{227}_{89}\text{Ac}$$

and

$$^{230}_{90}\text{Th}(n, \gamma)\,^{231}_{90}\text{Th} \xrightarrow[\text{25.6 hr.}]{-\beta^-} \,^{231}_{91}\text{Pa}$$

The metals are obtained by the same techniques used for the lanthanides (pp. 41–43). Except that their crystal structures are more complex and that in chemical reactions they yield a greater variety of oxidation states (Tables 5.2 and 5.3), the actinide metals are closely comparable to the lanthanide metals. Actinium is almost indistinguishable from lanthanum in its reactions and those of its ions, and thorium is very simi-·lar to cerium (p. 73). Protactinium, however, resembles the lanthanides closely only in its lower and less stable oxidation states. In the common +5 state, its chemistry is not markedly different from that of tantalum. Uranium(III) and uranium(IV) resemble, respectively, the tripositive lanthanides and tetrapositive cerium or thorium, except, of course, in the ease with which they are oxidized. The common uranium(VI) species is the linear uranyl, UO_2^{2+}, ion. This mildly oxidizing and readily complexed species has no parallel except with the comparable transuranium species NpO_2^{2+}, PuO_2^{2+}, AmO_2^{2+}.

Actinium and protactinium are too scarce to be of practical importance. Both thorium and uranium are useful in fission reactors. Nonnuclear applications include thorium in magnesium alloys and in gas-discharge and high-intensity lamps; thorium dioxide in high-emissivity cathodes and refractories; uranium in X-ray and vacuum tubes; and uranium compounds in pigments.

The Transuranium Elements. Typical nuclear reactions for the syntheses of these elements are summarized in Table 5.4.

TABLE 5.4. Nuclear Syntheses of Transuranium Elements

Symbol	Atomic number	Mass number	Reaction
Np	93	239	$^{238}_{92}U(n, \gamma)^{239}_{92}U \xrightarrow[23 \text{ min.}]{-\beta^-} {}^{239}_{93}Np$
Pu	94	239	$^{239}_{93}Np \xrightarrow[2.33 \text{ days}]{-\beta^-} {}^{239}_{94}Pu$
Am	95	241	$^{239}_{94}Pu(n, \gamma)^{240}_{94}Pu(n, \gamma)^{241}_{94}Pu \xrightarrow[13 \text{ yr.}]{-\beta^-} {}^{241}_{95}Am$
Cm	96	244	$^{241}_{94}Pu(n, \gamma)^{242}_{94}Pu(n, \gamma)^{243}_{94}Pu \xrightarrow[5 \text{ hr.}]{-\beta^-} {}^{243}_{95}Am$
			$^{243}_{95}Am(n, \gamma)^{244}_{95}Am \xrightarrow[26 \text{ min.}]{-\beta^-} {}^{244}_{96}Cm$
Bk	97	249	$^{244}_{96}Cm(n, \gamma)^{245}_{96}Cm(n, \gamma)^{246}_{96}Cm(n, \gamma)^{247}_{96}Cm$
			$^{247}_{96}Cm(n, \gamma)^{248}_{96}Cm(n, \gamma)^{249}_{96}Cm \xrightarrow[65 \text{ min.}]{-\beta^-} {}^{249}_{97}Bk$
Cf	98	250	$^{249}_{97}Bk(n, \gamma)^{250}_{97}Bk \xrightarrow[3.13 \text{ hr.}]{-\beta^-} {}^{250}_{98}Cf$
Es	99	253	$^{250}_{98}Cf(n, \gamma)^{251}_{98}Cf(n, \gamma)^{252}_{98}Cf$
			$^{252}_{98}Cf(n, \gamma)^{253}_{98}Cf \xrightarrow[20 \text{ days}]{-\beta^-} {}^{253}_{99}Es$
Fm	100	254	$^{253}_{99}Es(n, \gamma)^{254m}_{99}Es \xrightarrow[36 \text{ hr.}]{-\beta^-} {}^{254}_{100}Fm$
Md	101	256	$^{253}_{99}Es(\alpha, n)^{256}_{101}Md$
No	102	254	$^{246}_{96}Cm(^{12}_{6}C, 4n)^{254}_{102}No$
Lw	103	257	$^{250}_{98}Cf(^{11}_{5}B, 4n)^{257}_{103}Lw$

As a consequence of its ease of fission and reasonable half-life
(24,360 years), plutonium-239 has been prepared in very large
quantities. None of the others has been obtained in more than
small amounts; indeed, nuclear instability increases so rapidly
with increasing nuclear charge that no more than a few atoms
of the heaviest elements have been synthesized, and isolation
of measurable quantities has been limited to the ·Np-Cm
region. As atomic number increases, the stability of the tripositive state increases, and parallels with the lanthanides
become so striking that the known properties of the latter can
be used to predict quite exactly the properties of the comparable actinides. This is particularly true of the ion exchange

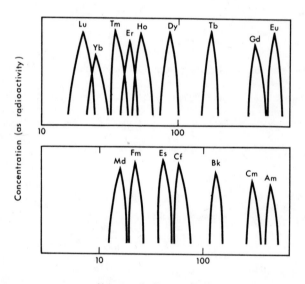

Volume of Eluate – drops

Fig. 5.3. Comparison of ion-exchange behavior of tri-positive lanthanides and
actinides with α-hydroxyisobutyrate. (Redrawn from Katz and Seaborg, *op. cit.*,
p. 435.)

techniques (pp. 80–88) used to isolate the species from target materials. The nature of this parallelism is shown in Fig. 5.3. Neptunium and plutonium resemble uranium closely both as metals and in their compounds. Divergence to true lanthanide behavior begins in the Am-Cm region. Applications are limited to the nuclear uses of plutonium.

In Conclusion

Thus ends our brief excursion into this fascinating area of chemistry. It is perhaps fitting to conclude by reminding the reader that the assistance in unraveling the chemistry of the actinides provided by the substantial background of information on the lanthanides is only another indication of the wisdom of applying the teachings and experiences of history to the solution of new problems.

Selected Readings

Asprey, L. B., and Cunningham, B. B., "Progress in Inorganic Chemistry," F. A. Cotton, Ed., Vol. 2, pp. 286–302. Interscience Publishers, New York, 1960. (Oxidation states.)

Cunningham, B. B., "XVIIth International Congress of Pure and Applied Chemistry," Vol. I, pp. 64–81, Butterworths, London, 1960. (Comparative chemistry of lanthanides and actinides.)

Cunningham, B. B., "Rare Earth Research," E. V. Kleber, Ed., pp. 127–34, The Macmillan Company, New York, 1961. (Comparative chemistry of lanthanides and actinides.)

Hampel, C. A., Ed., "Rare Metals Handbook," 2nd ed., Reinhold Publishing Corp., New York, 1961. (Plutonium, ch. 18; thorium, ch. 28; uranium, ch. 31.)

Katz, J. J., and Seaborg, G. T., "The Chemistry of the Actinide Elements," Methuen, London, John Wiley & Sons, New York, 1957. (Complete survey.)

Seaborg, G. T., and Katz, J. J., Eds., "The Actinide Elements," McGraw-Hill Book Company, New York, 1954. (Detailed survey.)

Weeks, M. E., "Discovery of the Elements," 6th ed., chs. 29, 31, Journal of Chemical Education, Easton, Pa., 1956. (History.)

INDEX